Quantitative Analysis of Gaseous Pollutants

Quantitative Analysis of Gaseous Pollutants

Walter E. Ruch, Ph.D.
Industrial Hygienist
Lawrence Radiation Laboratory
University of California
Livermore, California

ANN ARBOR ■ LONDON
ann arbor-humphrey science publishers

© 1970 by Ann Arbor-Humphrey Science Publishers, Inc.
Drawer No. 1425, 600 S. Wagner Road, Ann Arbor, Michigan 48106

Library of Congress Catalog Card No. 70–119743
SBN 250–39993–8
Printed in the United States of America
All Rights Reserved

Ann Arbor-Humphrey Science Publishers, Ltd.
5 Great Russell Street, London, W.C. 1, England

Foreword

Francis Bacon observed that "Some books are to be tasted, others to be swallowed, and some few to be chewed and digested." Were he writing today, he might add another category: that of the still fewer books to be worn as a wrist watch for ready consultation.

Such a book is Dr. Ruch's. Taking into account today's plethora of methods of air analysis for the increasing variety of gaseous contaminants—and the fact that the methods are being published in a widely diversified literature—an annotated bibliography becomes an essential tool.

It is true that *Chemical Abstracts* provides a tremendous source for analytical methods as these appear. But much beyond a chronological listing of abstracts is needed by the specialized group of scientists engaged in the evaluation of atmospheric contaminants for purposes of industrial hygiene or air pollution control. The applicable methods need to be grouped under headings of each of the contaminants to permit a comparison of the relative advantages. Specific information on each method needs to be included to guide the analyst in his decision about whether or not to proceed in what may be the not inconsiderable task of consulting the original reference. It is the inclusion of these helps to the investigator that constitutes the unique contribution of Dr. Ruch's book.

Following each reference is an initial statement offering that bit of information the analyst must first know—the concentration range for which the method is applicable. The analyst's decision to pursue a given method is directed by the express statement that that method is or is not suitable to purposes of industrial hygiene or air pollution. The concise presentation of pertinent factors of the procedure saves time for reviewing possible methods; and of much help in planning the time required for a prospective investigation is the author's estimate of the number of minutes or hours needed to complete the analysis.

Recollection of the difficulties involved in arriving at the optimum method or even an acceptable one in earlier years renders the value of this book of Dr. Ruch's even more impressive. Laborious digging into the literature during the 1920's brought to light a method for analyzing benzene vapor in air by nitration and subsequent quantitative reduction of the dinitrobenzene with stannous chloride. It required fortuitous correspondence with another early investigator to learn that tellurium trichloride was the preferable reducing agent. In the middle 1930's, an approach to provide the then current information on methods for air analysis was the publication of committee reports on inorganic contaminants in 1936 and on organic contaminants in 1937 in the *Year Book Supplement* of *The American Journal of Public Health*. These merely stated the essentials of the methods in a few words with a citation of the reference. How eagerly would those of us conducting air analysis for the comparatively few contaminants of those years have availed ourselves of such a book as Dr. Ruch's! With the many more contaminants of these days, the value of the book takes on a correspondingly greater importance as an essential in the armamentarium of the large number of investigators in this field—not only those newly entering this activity but those as well with an extensive background of experience.

Thus my extension of the quotation from Francis Bacon to the analogy with the wrist watch may claim the added pertinence of timeliness, and of its being up-to-the-minute in citation of the latest material on the subject of chemical analysis of airborne gases and vapors.

Ann Arbor, Michigan   Warren A. Cook
May, 1970   Professor of Industrial Health
                                        University of Michigan

Preface

This volume is designed for use as a quick reference source in the area of the microchemistry of airborne gases and vapors. Information is provided, whenever possible, about a basic outline of the method, sensitivity, sampling equipment and procedure, interferences, and approximate time required to complete a single analysis of a particular contaminant.

Industrial hygienists, air pollution people, and others who must analyze contaminants in the microcentration range can now use this book and find the reference for a suitable method, spending a few minutes instead of hours to find the original reference that provides a detailed description of the method chosen.

All the methods abstracted are in English and easily obtainable. They are all applicable to industrial hygiene work and many of them can be used in air pollution work, either in ambient air sampling or in stack gas sampling and analysis. Many of the contaminants listed here occur as air pollutants around specific industrial plants and therefore can be important in reactions occurring there. It must always be remembered that for these methods to be applicable to air pollution, long sampling times must often be used. This concentrates not only the constituent of interest but also any possible interferences from materials known to be present in the atmosphere in trace concentrations. In many cases this information is included in this book.

A conscious attempt has been made to keep the format of each abstract as similar to the others as possible to facilitate rapid scanning of each entry. If a group of methods appear in one source, they are abstracted and the original reference added whenever possible.

Livermore, California   W.E.R.
May, 1970

Contents

Acetaldehyde

Dal Nogare, S., T. D. Norris, and J. Mitchell, Jr. **Determination of Acetaldehyde and Acetone by the Iodoform Reaction,** Anal. Chem. **23,** 1473 (1951).

Acetaldehyde, in concentrations above 10 ppm in a 5-liter air sample, can be determined by this method. The air sample is collected in a fritted bubbler containing distilled water. It is then quantitatively transferred to a separatory funnel and reacted with a solution of iodine and sodium hydroxide. This procedure produces iodoform. Sodium thiosulfate is used to destroy the excess iodine, and the iodoform is extracted with chloroform. The absorbance of the resulting solution is read in a spectrophotometer at a wavelength of 347 mμ. The concentration of acetaldehyde is calculated from the quantity of iodoform produced.

The sampling rate through the fritted bubbler should be approximately 0.5 lpm for at least 10 minutes. A longer sampling time should increase the sensitivity obtainable with this method.

Interferences

Acetone, other methyl ketones, ethyl alcohol and isopropyl alcohol interfere with this method.

The method is simple, and analysis requires approximately 1 hour. It is suitable for industrial hygiene work but not sufficiently sensitive for air pollution work.

Ruch, J. E., and J. B. Johnson. **Determination of Aldehydes by Mercurimetric Oxidation,** Anal. Chem. **28,** 69 (1956).

Acetaldehyde, in the parts per million range, can be determined by this method. This method is not designed for air analysis and a sampling procedure must be devised. The sample is quantitatively transferred to an Erlenmeyer flask at which time 50 ml of a solution of potassium iodide in potassium hydroxide are added to the sample which is kept cool in an ice bath. Fifty ml of agar are added with 25

1

ml of glacial acetic acid. A standardized iodine solution is added, and after 15 minutes the sample is titrated with standardized thiosulfate solution. The quantity of aldehyde present is then calculated.

Sampling Procedure

No air sampling procedure has yet been developed.

Interferences

Alcohol and esters interfere slightly with this determination. Some vinyl compounds, unsaturated aldehydes, acetone, and methyl ethyl ketone also interfere slightly.

Sawicki E., T. R. Hauser, T. W. Stanley, and W. Elbert. **The 3-Methyl-2-Benzothiazolone Hydrozone Test. Sensitive New Methods for the Detection, Rapid Estimation and Determination of Aliphatic Aldehydes,** Anal. Chem. 33, 93 (1961).

Acetaldehyde can be analyzed in quantities as low as 5 μg per 100 ml of solution. Acetaldehyde, and other aliphatic aldehydes, can be determined specifically if only one of these compounds is present in the contaminated air.

Air is sampled through an impinger which contains a collecting solution of 10 ml of 3-methyl-2-benzothiazolone and distilled water. The solution is transferred to a volumetric flask and aqueous ferric chloride is added. The mixture is then diluted to 100 ml with acetone. The absorbance of the resulting blue color is read in a spectrophotometer at 670 mμ and the quantity of aldehyde present is read from a calibration curve.

Sampling Procedure

A sampling rate of 2 lpm through a midget impinger containing 10 ml of solution should be satisfactory for collection of the aldehyde.

Interferences

Other aliphatic aldehydes interfere, and if they exist singly in the air to be sampled they can be accurately determined by this method. Also thought to interfere are aniline, N-alkylanilines, N,N-dialkylanilines, indoles, carbazoles and phenothiazines.

The method is quantitative for acetaldehyde from a concentration of about 5–125 μg per 100 ml of solution. The method is applicable to air and auto exhaust analysis and requires approximately 30 minutes to complete.

Albrecht, A. M., W. I. Scher, Jr., and H. J. Vogel. **Determination of Aliphatic Aldehydes by Spectrophotometry,** Anal. Chem. **34,** 398 (1962).

Acetaldehyde can be determined quantitatively at concentrations below 0.4μ moles per ml of sampling solution.

The air sample may be collected in a midget impinger containing 10 ml of distilled water. To an aliquot of this sample a solution of methylamine hydrochloride in sodium pyrophosphate is added, followed by the addition of a solution of *o*-aminobenzaldehyde. The absorbance of the yellow-colored reaction mixture is read at 440 mμ in a spectrophotometer. The quantity present is read from a calibration curve.

The sampling rate may be 0.1 cfm through a midget impinger or 1 cfm through a standard impinger. Scrubbers or gas washing bottles may be used. A sampling duration of 30 minutes will usually collect a suitable sample.

Interferences

Other aliphatic aldehydes interfere and many of them can be determined by this method.

The method is useful for atmospheric sampling and analysis and should be adaptable for use at stack concentrations. Analysis requires approximately 1 hour.

Clancy, D. J., and D. E. Kramm. **Determination of Acetaldehyde by Colorimetry,** Anal. Chem. **35,** 1987 (1963).

Acetaldehyde, in concentrations as low as 1 ppm, can be determined by this method. The air sample can be collected in a midget or fritted bubbler containing 10 ml distilled water. An aliquot of the sample is checked for neutrality, and solutions of morpholine, acetic acid and sodium nitroprusside are added. The sample is diluted to a definite volume and allowed to stand for 3 hours. The transmittance of the resulting pink color is read in a spectrophotometer at 575 mμ. The concentration of the aldehyde is then read from a calibration curve.

Sampling Procedure

A sampling rate of 0.1 cfm should provide a satisfactory sampling rate through the impinger or bubbler.

Interferences

Formaldehyde, propionaldehyde, crotonaldehyde, acrolein, and glyoxal all exert some interfering influences.

The method is not sensitive enough for air pollution work but is applicable to industrial hygiene and areas where concentrations can be expected to exceed a few parts per million. Analysis requires about 4 hours but most of this period is used for color development.

Kwan, T. W., and B. M. Watts. **A New Color Reaction of Anthrone with Malonaldehyde and Other Aliphatic Aldehydes,** Anal. Chem. **35,** 733 (1963).

A method is described for the analysis of acetaldehyde using anthrone as the color-forming reagent. It appears to be applicable to air samples containing elevated concentrations of the aldehyde. More work needs to be done to determine sampling solutions, sampling rates, and sensitivities before this method can be used routinely.

Hashmi, M. H., and A. A. Ayaz. **The Determination of Methyl Ketones and Acetaldehydes by Titration with Hypobromite Using Bordeaux Indicator,** Anal. Chem. **36,** 385 (1964).

Acetaldehyde can be simply, accurately and rapidly determined with this method. The method, although not designed for air analysis, should be applicable with some modification. The sample could perhaps be collected in water using an impinger or a fritted bubbler. A measured aliquot of sample is placed in a flask, 3N sodium hydroxide is added, and the mixture is titrated against standard hypobromite solution using Bordeaux as an internal indicator. The end point shows up as a change from light pink to faint yellow or colorless.

A sampling rate of about 1–2 lpm should be adequate for collection of the sample.

Interferences

Aliphatic aldehydes and methyl ketones will interfere, as will high concentrations of aldehydes.

The method should have application in ambient air, industrial hygiene and stack gas analysis. Analysis should require less than 1 hour to complete.

Arsenault, G. P., and W. Yaphe. **Fructose-Resorcinol-Hydrochloric Acid Test for Detection and Determination of Acetaldehyde,** Anal. Chem. **38,** 503 (1966).

A simple rapid method for the determination of acetaldehyde is described. A sampling method needs to be devised before this procedure can be used for air analysis.

Acetates

Goddu, R. F., N. F. Le Blanc, and C. M. Wright. **Spectrophotometric Determination of Esters and Anhydrides by Hydroxamic Acid Reaction,** Anal. Chem. **27,** 1251 (1955).

See Also

Hill, V. T. Ind. Eng. Chem., Anal. Ed. **18,** 317 (1946).

Acetates, in concentrations above 20 ppm in a 25-liter air sample, can be determined by this method. The sample is collected in two fritted bubblers connected in series, each containing ethyl alcohol. The sample is reacted with an alkaline hydroxylamine solution. The addition of ferric ion to this mixture produces a highly colored product. The absorbance of this product is read at a wavelength of 530 mμ. The quantity of ester present is read from a calibration curve, and the airborne concentration is calculated.

Sampling Procedure

The air sample is collected in two fritted bubblers connected in series, each containing 10 ml ethyl alcohol. The sampling rate should be approximately 1–2 lpm until at least 25 liters of air have been sampled.

Interferences

Any other ester, anhydrides, aldehydes, and isocyanates will interfere with this determination.

Analysis requires approximately 2 hours to complete. The method is applicable to industrial hygiene analysis but is not sufficiently sensitive for air pollution.

Acetic Acid

Franklin, M., R. Scherberger, H. Brockmyre, and D. W. Fasset. **Determination of Acetic Acid in Air,** Am. Ind. Hyg. Assoc. J. Quart. **17,** 221 (1956).

Acetic acid, at concentrations below 1 ppm, can be determined by this method. The sample is collected in an impinger containing an absorbing solution of glycerol, water, methyl purple indicator and an antifoam agent. The absorbing solution is calibrated by titrating with acetic acid until the indicator color changes from the original green to purple. Air is sampled until this same color change takes place, and the concentration of acetic acid is calculated.

Sampling Procedure

A sampling rate of 0.1 cfm provides satisfactory collection when a midget impinger is used. At acid concentrations above 15 ppm the time required for the color change must be accurately noted because a few seconds error in recording the time of the appearance of the end point will cause an appreciable error. In order to overcome this difficulty it is possible to use larger volumes of absorbing solution or lower airflow rates.

Interferences

Most acids will react in the same manner; therefore, only one acid must be present in the atmosphere to be analyzed. Carbon dioxide does not interfere at concentrations below 5000 ppm.

The method is applicable to industrial hygiene analysis and requires less than 1 hour to complete.

Acetone

Greenburg, L. A., and D. Lester. **A Micromethod for the Determination of Acetone and Ketone Bodies,** J. Biol. Chem. **154,** 177 (1944).

A colorimetric method is described for the determination of acetone in concentrations above 0.04 ppm. The sample is collected in 2,4-dinitrophenylhydrazine, treated with carbon tetrachloride and sodium hydroxide, and read in a spectrophotometer at a wavelength of 420 mμ.

Hashmi, M. H., and A. A. Ayaz. **The Determination of Methyl Ketones and Acetaldehydes by Titration with Hypobromite Using Bordeaux Indicator,** Anal. Chem. **36,** 385 (1964).

Acetone can be simply, accurately and rapidly determined with this method. The method, although not designed for air analysis, should be applicable with some modification. The sample could perhaps be collected in water using an impinger or a fritted bubbler. A measured aliquot of sample is placed in a flask, 3N sodium hydroxide is added, and the mixture is titrated against standard hypobromite solution using Bordeaux as an internal indicator. The end point shows up as a change from light pink to faint yellow or colorless.

A sampling rate of about 1–2 lpm should be adequate for collection of the sample.

Interferences

Aliphatic aldehydes and methyl ketones will interfere, as will high concentrations of aldehydes.

The method should have application in ambient air, industrial hygiene and stack gas analysis. Analysis should require less than 1 hour to complete.

Jacobs, M. B. *The Analytical Chemistry of Industrial Poisons, Hazards and Solvents,* 2nd ed. (New York: Interscience Publishers, Inc., 1949), p 685.

See Also
1. Messinger, J. J. Soc. Chem. Ind. **18,** 138 (1889).
2. Goodwin, L. F. J. Am. Chem. Soc. **42,** 39 (1920).

Acetone, in the parts per million range, can be determined by this method. The air sample can be collected in a gas washing bottle containing a standardized sodium hydroxide solution. After collection, 25 ml of the sample is quantitatively transferred to a stoppered Erlenmeyer flask along with 25 ml of water and 35 ml of a standardized iodine solution. After 15 minutes hydrochloric acid is added, and the excess iodine is titrated with a standardized sodium thiosulfate solution. The airborne concentration of acetone is calculated.

Sampling Procedure

The sample is collected in a gas washing bottle containing 50 ml of standardized sodium hydroxide solution at a rate of 1–3 lpm. The sampling duration will depend upon the concentration expected.

Interferences

Any material reacting with iodine will interfere with the analysis.

The method is suitable for industrial hygiene work but is not sufficiently sensitive for air pollution work. Analysis requires approximately 1 hour to complete.

Hanson, N. W., D. A. Reilly, and H. E. Stagg, Eds. *The Determination of Toxic Substances in Air* (Cambridge, England: W. Heffer and Sons Ltd., 1965) p 40.

Acetone, in concentrations ranging from 50–2500 ppm in a 1-liter air sample, can be determined quickly and accurately by this method. Both upper and lower concentration limits can be changed by simply changing the volume of air sampled.

The air sample is collected in a midget impinger containing distilled water. Following collection the sample is quantitatively transferred to an Erlenmeyer flask. Sodium hydroxide is added to the flask, which is then sealed and placed in an ice bath. Standardized iodine is added to the sample in 0.5-ml increments until the total addition is 5 ml. After the sample is in the ice bath for 10 minutes, hydrochloric acid is added and the sample titrated with standardized sodium thiosulfate. A starch solution is used as the indicator and a blank is titrated simultaneously.

Sampling Procedure

The sampling rate through the midget impinger containing distilled water should be approximately 1 lpm, but even at this rate the collection efficiency is only about 80%. When calculating the airborne concentration, this efficiency must be taken into consideration.

Interferences

Any material reacting with iodine or thiosulfate will interfere with this titrimetric procedure.

This method is relatively simple and rapid, requiring less than 1 hour for analysis. No special or expensive equipment is required. This method is suitable for industrial hygiene work. It is not considered sensitive enough for air pollution work even though concentrations in the range of 1 ppm can be determined by extending the sampling time.

Acetylene

Hughes, E. E., and Ralph Gorden, Jr. **Determination of Acetylene in Air in Concentrations from Ten Parts per Billion to Ten Parts per Million,** Anal. Chem. **31,** 94 (1959).

Acetylene, in concentrations ranging from ten parts per billion to ten parts per million, can be determined by this method. The air sample is collected on purified silica gel contained in narrow diameter glass tubes which are maintained at the temperature of dry ice to promote the adsorption of acetylene. Following collection, the sample is allowed to stand at room temperature for 3 minutes to allow the acetylene to diffuse through the silica gel. A small quantity of a reagent consisting of one part ammoniacal cupric chloride and two parts hydroxylamine hydrochloride is added to the silica gel. The resulting pink to red color produced in the presence of acetylene is compared with silica gel tubes containing known concentrations of acetylene.

Sampling Procedure

The air sample is collected in small glass tubes containing silica gel maintained at the temperature of dry ice. The sampling rate can range from 50–200 ml per minute depending on the acetylene concentration expected. A 30-minute sample will usually provide a sufficient sample.

Interferences

The method is not specific for acetylene but will determine any alkyne where the triple bond occurs at the end of a chain. Water vapor can deactivate the silica gel and should be removed by including a trap, maintained at dry ice temperatures, in front of the collecting tube. Other interfering substances include hydrogen sulfide and some mercaptans.

The method is quantitative in the range of ten parts per billion to ten parts per million. No special or expensive equipment is required. This method is suitable for air pollution as well as industrial hygiene work. It requires approximately 1 hour for complete analysis.

Acrolein

Circle, S. J., L. Stone, and C. S. Boruff. **Acrolein Determination by Means of Tryptophan. A Colorimetric Micromethod,** Ind. Eng. Chem., Anal. Ed. **17,** 259 (1945).

Acrolein, in the range of 15–150 µg per aliquot to be analyzed, can be determined by this method. In order to adapt this method to air analysis, a sampling method must be devised. Collection in 95% ethyl alcohol or perhaps water appears to be feasible. The sample could be collected in midget impingers or fritted glass bubblers. A 2-ml aliquot is used for analysis. A tryptophan in hydrochloric acid solution and ice cold 12N hydrochloric acid are added to the sample. The color is developed by heating in a water bath for 50 minutes. The absorbance of the blue color produced is read in a spectrophotometer at 555 mμ.

Sampling Procedure

A sampling rate of about 0.1 cfm should be satisfactory for use with the impinger or bubbler containing 10 ml of sampling solution.

Interferences

Other aldehydes such as formaldehyde and acetaldehyde interfere with this determination.

The method is quantitative in the range of 15–150 µg per aliquot and requires about 2 hours to complete. Strict attention must be paid to the order of reagent addition and the temperature at which the reactions occur. It is also necessary that the 2-ml aliquot used for analysis contain 15–150 µg for analysis.

The method should be suitable for industrial hygiene analysis. With some modifications, it could probably be applied to stack gas analysis. The method is not sensitive enough for air pollution work.

Jacobs, M. B. *The Analytical Chemistry of Industrial Poisons, Hazards and Solvents,* 2nd ed. (New York: Interscience Publishers, Inc., 1949), p 680.

Acrolein, in the parts per million range, can be determined by this method. The sample is collected in two bubblers connected in series and containing absolute ethyl alcohol. The bubblers should be maintained in an ice bath to prevent loss of alcohol by evaporation. The sample is quantitatively transferred to a volumetric flask and diluted to the mark with ethyl alcohol. A 10-ml aliquot is used for analysis. A solution of benzidine in acetic acid is added to the sample and the standards, which are then heated in a water bath for 15 minutes. The color of the sample is compared to that of the standards, and the airborne concentration of acrolein is calculated.

Sampling Procedure

The sample is collected in two fritted bubblers containing absolute ethyl alcohol at a rate of 0.5 lpm for a duration dictated by the expected concentration.

Interferences

Analysis requires approximately 1 hour to complete. The method is suitable for industrial hygiene analysis but is not sufficiently sensitive for air pollution work.

Ruch, J. E., and J. B. Johnson. **Determination of Aldehydes by Mercurimetric Oxidation,** Anal. Chem. **28,** 69 (1956).

Acrolein, in the parts per million range, can be determined by this method. This method is not designed for air analysis, and a sampling procedure must be devised. The sample is quantitatively transferred to an Erlenmeyer flask at which time 50 ml of a solution of potassium iodide in potassium hydroxide are added. The sample is kept cool in an ice bath. Then 50 ml of agar and 25 ml of glacial acetic acid are added. A standardized iodine solution is then added, and after 15 minutes the sample is titrated with standardized thiosulfate solution. The quantity of aldehyde present is then calculated.

Sampling Procedure

No air sampling procedure has yet been developed.

Interferences

Alcohol and esters interfere slightly with this determination. Some vinyl compounds, unsaturated aldehydes, acetone, and methyl ethyl ketone also interfere slightly.

Elkins, H. B. *The Chemistry of Industrial Toxicology,* 2nd ed. (New York: John Wiley and Sons, Inc., 1959), p 290.

Acrolein, in concentrations above 0.15 ppm, can be determined by this method if a 50-liter air sample is collected. The sample is collected in two petri bubblers, series connected. After collection, the sampling solutions are quantitatively transferred to Erlenmeyer flasks. A 10-ml aliquot is reacted with benzidine in glacial acetic acid and heated in a water bath. The transmission of the sample is read in a spectrophotometer equipped with a 46 filter. The quantity of acrolein present in the sample is determined from a calibration curve. The airborne concentration is then calculated.

Sampling Procedure

The sample is collected in two bubblers, series connected, each containing isopropyl alcohol. While sampling, the bubblers are maintained in dry ice. A sampling rate of 2 lpm is adequate and at least 50 liters of air should be collected.

Interferences

Other aldehydes and compounds forming acrolein may interfere.
Analysis requires less than 1 hour to complete. The method is applicable to industrial hygiene work.

Cohen, I. R., and A. P. Altshuller.   **A New Spectrophotometric Method for the Determination of Acrolein in Combustion Gases and in the Atmosphere,** Anal. Chem. **33,** 726 (1961).

Acrolein, in concentrations exceeding 0.1 ppm, can be determined by this method. The sample can be collected in ethyl alcohol contained in two fritted bubblers connected in series. The sampling procedure involves collection of the sample directly in the color-forming reagent at room temperature. Fritted bubblers are again used.

Analysis of the sample collected in ethyl alcohol involves adding the color-forming reagent 4-hexylresorcinol–mercuric chloride–trichloroacetic acid–ethyl alcohol to the sample. The resulting solution is heated and cooled. The absorbance of the blue-colored product is read at 605 $m\mu$ in a spectrophotometer and compared with standards.

Sampling Procedure

The sampling rate through two fritted bubblers containing 10 ml of sampling solution each should not exceed 2 lpm. A sampling duration of 5 minutes is usually sufficient.

Interferences

The method is essentially specific for acrolein but is not applicable for concentrations below 0.1 ppm because passing more than 10 liters of air through the alcohol produces a low collection efficiency.

The method is applicable to atmospheric as well as auto exhaust samples. Analysis requires approximately 1 hour to complete.

Sawicki, E., T. R. Hauser, T. W. Stanley, and W. Elbert. **The 3-Methyl-2-Benzothiazolone Hydrozone Test. Sensitive New Methods for the Detection, Rapid Estimation and Determination of Aliphatic Aldehydes,** Anal. Chem. 33, 93 (1961).

Acrolein can be analyzed in quantities as low as 5 μg per 100 ml of solution. Acrolein, and other aliphatic aldehydes, can be determined specifically if only one of these compounds is present in the contaminated air.

Air is sampled through an impinger which contains a collecting solution of 10 ml of 3-methyl-2-benzothiazolone and distilled water. The solution is transferred to a volumetric flask and aqueous ferric chloride is added. The mixture is then diluted to 100 ml with acetone. The absorbance of the resulting blue color is read in a spectrophotometer at 670 mμ and the quantity of aldehyde present is read from a calibration curve.

Sampling Procedure

A sampling rate of 2 lpm through a midget impinger containing 10 ml of solution is satisfactory for collection of the aldehyde.

Interferences

Other aliphatic aldehydes interfere, and if they exist singly in the air to be sampled they can be accurately determined by this method. Also thought to interfere are aniline, N-alkylanilines, N,N-dialkylanilines, indoles, carbozoles and phenothiazines.

The method is quantitative for acrolein from a concentration of about 5–125 μg per 100 ml of solution. The method is applicable to air and auto exhaust analysis and requires approximately 30 minutes to complete the analysis.

Kwan, T. W., and B. M. Watts. **A New Color Reaction of Anthrone with Malonaldehyde and Other Aliphatic Aldehydes,** Anal. Chem. 35, 733 (1963).

A method is described for the analysis of acrolein using anthrone as the color-forming reagent. The method appears to be applicable to air samples containing elevated concentrations of the aldehyde. More work needs to be done to determine sampling solution, sampling rates and sensitivities before the method can be used routinely.

Alcorn, R. A. **Fluorometric Determination of Acrolein and Related Compounds with *m*-Aminophenol,** Anal. Chem. **40,** 1704 (1968).

Acrolein, in concentrations above approximately 0.002 μg/ml, can be determined by this method. A 2-ml aliquot of the sample is quantitatively transferred to a test tube with *m*-aminophenol and hydroxylamine hydrochloride in hydrochloric acid. If the sample is collected in water, it is heated for 10 minutes in boiling water; if collected in ethyl alcohol it is heated for 45 minutes at 65°C. After cooling, the fluorescence of the sample is read at a wavelength of 495 mμ. The quantity of acrolein present is read from a calibration curve and the airborne concentration calculated.

Sampling Procedure

This method was not designed specifically for air analysis but should be applicable particularly to air pollution work because of the sensitivity of the technique. It appears to be possible to collect the sample in ethyl alcohol or water in a midget impinger for a period exceeding 10 minutes. If the sample is collected in water, two impingers in series should be used. If the sample is collected in ethyl alcohol, the impinger should be immersed in an ice bath to minimize evaporative losses.

Interferences

Other aldehydes and compounds producing acrolein after hydrolysis interfere with this determination.

Analysis requires approximately 2 hours to complete. This method should be applicable to both industrial hygiene and air pollution work.

Acrylonitrile

Peterson, G. W., and H. H. Radke. **Determination of Small Amounts of Acrylonitrile in Air,** Ind. Eng. Chem., Anal. Ed. **16,** 63 (1944).

Acrylonitrile, in concentrations above 25 ppm, can be analyzed by this method. The sample is collected in two absorption traps each containing glass beads to a depth of one inch and 2 ml of sulfuric acid. The absorbers are connected in series and placed in an ice bath. Air is sampled through this arrangement at 0.4 lpm until about 6 mg of acrylonitrile have been collected. The acid sample is made alkaline with sodium hydroxide. Hydrogen peroxide is added and the sample is distilled into 0.025N sulfuric acid. The excess sulfuric acid is titrated with sodium hydroxide using methyl red as the indicator.

Interferences

No mention is made of any possible interfering materials but with the distillation procedure used the method should have good specificity.

The procedure requires about 2 hours for completion and is suitable for industrial hygiene work. The method is not sufficiently sensitive for air pollution work.

Gisclard, J. B., D. B. Robinson, and P. J. Kuczt. **A Rapid Empirical Procedure for the Determination of Acrylonitrile and Acrylic Esters in the Atmosphere,** Am. Ind. Hyg. Assoc. J. **19,** 43 (1958).

Acrylonitrile, in concentrations above approximately 10 ppm, can be determined by this method. The air sample is collected in a midget impinger equipped with a specially constructed suction device. Any suction device can be used provided a flow rate of 300 ml can be maintained through the impinger. The impinger contains potassium permanganate, sodium hydroxide, and telluric acid. A 200-ml air sample is pulled through the impinger and sampling solution in 20 seconds. The air sample is collected in this same manner until the permanganate changes color from pink to bluish-green. The concentration of solvent is then determined from a calibration curve showing air volume versus parts per million.

Interferences

Any compound containing double-bonded carbon atoms may interfere with this determination.

The method is suitable for industrial hygiene field work but is empirical in nature and judgment must be exercised when basing recommendations on data provided by this analysis. The method requires about 30 minutes for completion.

Gunther, F. A., and R. C. Blinn. *Analysis of Insecticides and Acaricides* (New York: Interscience Publishers, Inc., 1955), p 265.

Acrylonitrile, in concentrations exceeding 0.5–1.0 ppm, can be determined quickly and accurately by this method. The air sample is collected in an absorber containing sulfuric acid over glass beads. Collection efficiency is increased by using two absorbers in series. During the sampling procedure the absorbers must be kept in an ice bath. After collection the sample is quantitatively transferred to a refluxing apparatus; copper acetate is added to inhibit any polymerization. The sample is made alkaline with sodium hydroxide and oxidized with hydrogen peroxide while refluxing gently. This procedure converts the sample first to acetamide and then to ammonia. After 30 minutes the sample is distilled over and titrated with a standard sodium hydroxide solution. The concentration of acrylonitrile is calculated.

Sampling Procedure

The sampling rate for the collection of acrylonitrile should not exceed 0.4 lpm because above this value the collection efficiency drops rapidly. The collection period should be such that approximately 6 mg of acrylonitrile are collected.

Interferences

The method is not specific for acrylonitrile, and many nitrogen-containing compounds will interfere with the determination.

The determination is simple, rapid, requires no special or expensive equipment, and is suitable for analysis of acrylonitrile as an airborne pesticide as well as industrial hygiene work. The method requires about 2 hours for completion.

Hanson, N. W., D. A. Reilly, and H. E. Stagg, Eds. *The Determination of Toxic Substances in Air* (Cambridge, England: W. Heffer and Sons, Ltd., 1965), p 41.

See Also
1. Beesing, D. W., W. P. Tyler, D. M. Kurtz, and S. A. Harrison. Anal. Chem. **21**, 1073 (1949).
2. Haslam, J., and G. Newlands. Analyst, **80**, 50 (1955).

Acrylonitrile, in concentrations ranging from 5–50 ppm in an air sample of 15 liters, can be determined quickly and easily by this method. The air sample is collected in two midget impingers connected in series, each containing a solution of lauryl mercaptan in isopropyl alcohol. During the sampling procedure the impingers should be kept in an ice bath. After collection the sample is quantitatively added to a 50-ml volumetric flask. Alcoholic potassium hydroxide, glacial acetic acid, and enough iodine to be exactly equivalent to the amount of lauryl mercaptan present are added to the samples. The optical density of the sample is read in a spectrophotometer at 425 mμ. The quantity of acrylonitrile present in the sample is read from a previously prepared calibration curve, and the airborne concentration is calculated.

Sampling Procedure

The sampling rate through the two midget impingers containing 10 ml of lauryl mercaptan should be approximately 1 lpm. The sampling duration should be 15 minutes or of sufficient length to collect a sample that will provide a suitable sensitivity.

Interferences

No interferences are given.

This method is relatively simple and rapid, requiring about 1.5 hours for analysis. No special or expensive equipment is required, and the method is suitable for industrial hygiene work. The method is not considered sufficiently sensitive for air pollution work.

Alcohols

Hoare, D. E., and R. R. Ogilvie. **Spectrophotometric Method for the Microdetermination of Monohydric Aliphatic Alcohols,** Anal. Chem. **38,** 1799 (1966).

This method was not designed for air analysis but appears to be applicable. Monohydric aliphatic alcohols in concentrations exceeding approximately 0.1 μg per ml can be determined by this method. The sample may be collected in a midget impinger containing water. An 8-ml aliquot of the sample along with an acetate buffer and sodium nitrite solution are quantitatively transferred to a 50-ml flask.

The sample is incubated at 18°C for 30 minutes after which heptane is added and again incubated at 18° and agitated. The sample is cooled to 0°C and transferred to a cold separatory funnel and the aqueous layer removed. The heptane layer is transferred to a test tube and exposed to calcium chloride to remove water. The sample is reacted with α-naphthylamine and incubated at 18°C for 10 minutes. The color is allowed to develop while the sample is contained in a water bath at 60°C for 30 minutes. After cooling, the absorbance of the resulting solution is read in a spectrophotometer at 550 mμ. The concentration present in the sample is read from a calibration curve and the airborne concentration calculated.

Sampling Procedure

The sample is collected in a fritted bubbler at a rate of 2 lpm. Water may be used as the sampling solution.

Interferences

The method is not specific for monohydric aliphatic alcohols but determines many of them.

The method requires approximately 3 hours for analysis and is suitable for industrial hygiene work.

Jaselskis, B., and J. P. Warriner. **Titrametric Determination of Primary and Secondary Alcohols by Xenon Trioxide Oxidation,** Anal. Chem. **38,** 563 (1966).

Primary and secondary alcohols, in concentrations above 30 μg, can be determined by this method. An aliquot of the sample containing at least 30 μg of alcohol is quantitatively transferred to an Erlenmeyer flask. The sample is diluted to 20 ml and a known quantity of xenon trioxide standard solution is added. After 2 hours, several drops of sulfuric acid and sodium iodide are added to liberate the triiodide ion. The quantity of xenon trioxide used during the oxidation equals the difference between the xenon trioxide before reaction and after reaction with the alcohol. The quantity of alcohol present is determined from a calibration curve and the airborne concentration calculated.

Sampling Procedure

The sample is collected in a fritted bubbler, containing distilled water, at a rate of 2.8 lpm until 30 μg are collected.

Interferences

Halides, amines, carboxylic acids, ketones, and aldehydes interfere with this determination.

Analysis requires approximately 4 hours to complete. The method is suitable for industrial hygiene analysis but is probably not sensitive enough for air pollution work.

Scoggins, M. W., and J. W. Miller. **Ultraviolet Spectrophotometric Determination of Tertiary Alcohols by Conversion to Alkyl Iodides,** Anal. Chem. **38,** 612 (1966).

Tertiary alcohols, in the parts per million range, can be determined by this method. The method is not designed for air analysis but appears to be suitable for this application. It seems to be possible to collect the sample in cyclohexane. The sample is quantitatively transferred to an Erlenmeyer flask and reacted with hydriodic acid. The sample is transferred to a separatory funnel and washed with distilled water. The water layer is discarded and sodium hydroxide and hydrogen peroxide are added to the sample. The absorbance of the sample is read in a spectrophotometer at a wavelength of 268 mμ. The quantity of tertiary alcohol present is read from a calibration curve, and the airborne concentration is calculated.

Sampling Procedure

The sample is collected in cyclohexane. This sampling might have to be done in an ice bath to prevent evaporation of the cyclohexane. A sampling rate of 2.8 lpm through a fritted bubbler should collect an adequate sample.

Interferences

Any material that contains or produces CH_3CO groups will interfere with this determination. Olefins and aromatic compounds will also interfere.

Analysis requires approximately 15 minutes to complete. The method appears to be suitable for industrial hygiene work but is not sensitive enough for air pollution work.

Konishi, K., Y. Mori, H. Inoue, and M. Nozol. **Volumetric Determination of Alcohols in Aqueous Solution with Bromine Chloride**, Anal. Chem. **40**, 2198 (1968).

Primary and secondary alcohols in concentrations above 100 μg per ml can be determined by this method. An aliquot of the sample is reacted with bromine chloride, hydrochloric acid, and potassium iodide solution. The mixture is heated at 50°C for 3 hours. The liberated iodine is titrated with standardized sodium thiosulfate. Secondary alcohols require incubation for 1.5 hours at 20°C.

Sampling Procedure

The method was not designed for air analysis but appears to be applicable. The sample could be collected in distilled water in a midget impinger at a rate of 2.5 lpm.

Interferences

The method is not specific and all primary and secondary alcohols will react in the same manner.

Aldehydes

Ruch, J. E., and J. B. Johnson. **Determination of Aldehydes by Mercurimetric Oxidation,** Anal. Chem. 28, 69 (1956).

Aldehydes, in the parts per million range, can be determined by this method. This method is not designed for air analysis and a sampling procedure must be devised. The sample is quantitatively transferred to an Erlenmeyer flask and 50 ml of a solution of potassium iodide in potassium hydroxide are added. The sample is kept cool in an ice bath, and 50 ml of agar and 25 ml of glacial acetic acid are added. A standardized iodine solution is then added, and after 15 minutes the sample is titrated with standardized thiosulfate solution. The quantity of aldehyde present is then calculated.

Sampling Procedure

No air sampling procedure has yet been developed.

Interferences

Alcohol and esters interfere slightly with this determination. Some vinyl compounds, unsaturated aldehydes, acetone, and methyl ethyl ketone also interfere slightly.

Sawicki, E., T. R. Hauser, T. W. Stanley, and W. Elbert. **The 3-Methyl-2-Benzothiazolone Hydrozone Test. Sensitive New Methods for the Detection, Rapid Estimation and Determination of Aliphatic Aldehydes,** Anal. Chem. 33, 93 (1961).

Aliphatic aldehydes, determined as formaldehyde, can be analyzed in quantities as low as 5 μg per 100 ml of solution. Formaldehyde, and other aliphatic aldehydes, can be determined specifically if only one of these compounds is present in the contaminated air.

Air is sampled through an impinger which contains a collecting solution of 10 ml of 3-methyl-2-benzothiazolone and distilled water. The solution is transferred to a volumetric flask and aqueous ferric chloride is added. The mixture is then diluted to 100 ml with acetone. The absorbance of the resulting blue color is read in a spectrophotometer at 670 mμ and the quantity of aldehyde present is read from a calibration curve.

Sampling Procedure

A sampling rate of 2 lpm through a midget impinger containing 10 ml of solution should be satisfactory for collection of the aldehyde.

Interferences

Other aliphatic aldehydes interfere, and if they exist singly in the air to be sampled they can be accurately determined by this method. Also thought to interfere are aniline, N-alkylanilines, N,N-dialkylanilines, indoles, carbazoles and phenothiazines.

The method is quantitative for formaldehyde from a concentration of 5–125 μg per 100 ml of solution. The method is applicable to air and auto exhaust analysis and requires approximately 30 minutes to complete the analysis.

Hauser, T. R., and R. L. Cummins. **Increasing Sensitivity of 3-Methyl-2-Benzothiazolone Hydrazone Test for Analysis of Aliphatic Aldehydes in Air,** Anal. Chem. **36,** 679 (1964).

Aliphatic aldehydes, determined as formaldehyde, can be quantitatively determined in the parts per billion range. The air sample is collected in a bubbler containing an aqueous 3-methyl-2-benzothiazolone hydrazone. After collection the sample is allowed to stand for 1 hour for complete reaction to take place. Solutions of sulfamic acid and ferric chloride are added to an aliquot of the sample. The absorbance of the resulting solution is read in a spectrophotometer at 628 mμ. The concentration present is read from a calibration curve.

Sampling Procedure

The sampling rate is 0.5 lpm until at least 7.5 μg have been collected.

Interferences

No interferences are mentioned.

The analysis is applicable to any area where low concentrations of aliphatic aldehydes may be found. Analysis requires about 1.5 hours.

Allyl Alcohol

Jacobs, Morris B. *The Analytical Chemistry of Industrial Poisons, Hazards and Solvents,* 2nd ed. (New York: Interscience Publishers, Inc., 1949), p 625.

Allyl alcohol, in the parts per million range, can be determined by this method. The sample is collected in a fritted bubbler containing distilled water. A sampling rate appropriate for the particular bubbler selected must be used. The trapped alcohol is oxidized with a chromic–sulfuric acid solution. The acrolein produced by this reaction is determined by methods described elsewhere in this volume.

Interferences

Acrolein and other unsaturated alcohols oxidizable to acrolein will interfere with this determination.

Amines, Aliphatic

Hong, W. H., and K. A. Conners. *Spectrophotometric Determination of Aliphatic Amines by Acylation with Cinnamic Anhydride,* Anal. Chem. **40,** 1273 (1968).

Aliphatic amines, in concentrations at the parts per million level, can be determined by this method. This method was not designed specifically for air analysis but appears to be applicable. A 1-ml aliquot of the sample is quantitatively transferred to a 50-ml volumetric flask. Cinnamic anhydride solution and tri-*n*-butylamine in acetonitrile are added, mixed and allowed to react at room temperature for several minutes. Sodium hydroxide is added to the 50-ml mark and allowed to stand for 10 minutes. The sample mixture is quantitatively transferred to a separatory funnel and extracted with chloroform. The chloroform extract is washed with distilled water and filtered into a 50-ml volumetric flask. The sample is made to volume with chloroform, and the absorbance of the sample is read in a spectrophotometer at the proper wavelength for the particular amine of interest. The airborne concentration of amine is calculated.

Sampling Procedure

An air sampling procedure must be developed. Collection might be accomplished using a fritted bubbler containing an acetonitrile solution.

Interferences

Any aliphatic amine will interfere with this method.

Amines, Aromatic

Daniel, J. W. **The Determination of Aromatic Amino Compounds,** Analyst **86,** 640 (1961).

Five coupling agents are investigated to determine their efficiency in producing a colored azo-compound with aromatic amines at the parts per million level. The agents investigated were 2-naphthol-3,6-disulphonic acid, *N*-sulphatoethyl-*n*-toluidine, 3-hydroxy-2-naphthoic acid, *N*-1-naphthylethylenediamine, and *N*-diethyl-*N*-1-naphthylpropylenediamine.

The last three reagents provide approximately the same sensitivity for the determination of the aromatic amines. Methods are detailed for the quantitative determination of aromatic amines.

Stewart, J. T., T. D. Shaw, and A. B. Ray. **Spectrophotometric Determination of Primary Aromatic Amines with 9-Chloroacridine,** Anal. Chem. **41,** 360 (1969).

This method was not designed for air analysis but appears to be modifiable for this use. Most of these amines have some vapor pressure; therefore, this analysis is abstracted here.

Primary aromatic amines in concentrations above 10^{-7} moles can be determined by this method. The sample can be collected in ethyl alcohol. After collection, a 1-ml aliquot of the amine is quantitatively transferred to a volumetric flask. A solution of 9-chloroacridine is added and the pH is adjusted to 4.0 with hydrochloric acid. The absorbance of the resulting orange-colored solution is read in a spectrophotometer at 435 mμ.

Sampling Procedure

The sample may be collected in a fritted bubbler at a rate of 2 lpm.

Interferences

Primary amines and acridine will interfere with this determination. Complete analysis requires approximately 1 hour. The method is suitable for industrial hygiene work.

Ammonia

Gunther, F. A., J. H. Barkley, M. J. Kolbezen, R. C. Blinn, and E. A. Staggs. **Quantitative Microdetermination of Gaseous Ammonia by Its Absorption at 204.3 mμ,** Anal. Chem. **28,** 1985 (1956).

Ammonia, in concentrations from 7–1000 ppm, can be determined by this method. Air sampling methods as well as the detailed analytical method are described.

Elkins, H. B. *The Chemistry of Industrial Toxicology,* 2nd ed. (New York: John Wiley and Sons, Inc., 1959), p 292.

Ammonia, in concentrations above 3 ppm in a 50-l air sample, can be determined by this method. The sample is collected in a midget impinger containing a sulfuric acid solution. After collection, the sample is diluted to 50 ml with distilled water, and a 1-ml aliquot is transferred to a Nessler tube, where Nessler's reagent is added and the sample diluted to 50 ml. The sample is compared visually or spectrophotometrically with a set of standards, and the quantity of ammonia present in the sample is determined. The airborne concentration is calculated.

Sampling Procedure

The sample may be collected in a midget impinger containing 10 ml of a dilute sulfuric acid solution. A sampling rate of 1–3 lpm is satisfactory. A 50-liter air sample should be collected.

Interferences

Any material producing ammonia and some amines will interfere with this determination.

Analysis requires less than 1 hour to complete. This method is suitable for industrial hygiene work but is not sensitive enough for air pollution work.

Zitomer, F., and J. L. Lambert. **Spectrophotometric Determination of Ammonia as Trichloramine,** Anal. Chem. **34,** 1738 (1962).

Ammonia, in the concentration range of 10–300 ppm, can be quantitatively determined by this method. The air sample may be collected in an impinger containing distilled water. A sodium acetate–acetic acid buffer is added to the sample. Following this a hypochlorite solution, a nitrite solution, and a cadmium iodide–starch reagent are added. The absorbance of the resulting blue complex is read at 615 mμ and the quantity of ammonia is read from a calibration curve.

Sampling Procedure

The sampling rate may be 0.1 cfm through a midget impinger containing 10 ml of distilled water or 1 cfm through a standard impinger containing 100 ml of distilled water.

Interferences

Aromatic and aliphatic amines, iodide, and bromide may interfere with the determination of ammonia.

The method is applicable to ammonia in air determinations. The determination requires 1–2 hours for completion.

Hanson, N. W., D. A. Reilly, and H. E. Stagg, Eds. *The Determination of Toxic Substances in Air* (Cambridge, England: W. Heffer and Sons, Ltd., 1965), p 43.

Ammonia, in concentrations ranging from 10–1000 ppm, can be determined by this method. The air sample is collected in a midget impinger containing ammonia-free water and 1 ml Nessler's reagent. A suitable aliquot of the sample is placed in a Nessler tube, Nessler's reagent is added, and the sample is diluted to 50 ml. The colors produced are compared visually with a series of standards prepared from ammonium chloride, and the concentration of ammonia in air is calculated.

Sampling Procedure

The sampling rate through the midget impinger containing water and Nessler's reagent should be 0.2–0.25 lpm. The duration of sampling depends upon the expected concentration and is continued until a suitable color is seen.

Interferences

The method is considered to be specific for ammonia.

This method is simple and rapid, requiring about 30 minutes for completion. No special or expensive equipment is required, and the method is suitable for industrial hygiene work. The method is not considered sensitive enough for air pollution work.

Jacobs, Morris B. *The Analytical Toxicology of Industrial Inorganic Poisons* (New York: Interscience Publishers, Inc., 1967), p 610.

Ammonia, in concentrations above approximately 0.5 parts per million parts of air, can be determined by this method. The air sample can be collected in either two gas washing bottles or fritted bubblers connected in series containing a standardized sulfuric acid solution. After being collected, the sample is quantitatively transferred to a flask and titrated with a standardized sodium hydroxide solution to a methyl red end point. The airborne concentration of ammonia is calculated.

Sampling Procedure

A sampling rate of approximately 1 cfm through the fritted bubbler for 30 minutes should be adequate to collect a suitable sample.

Interferences

Any acidic or basic material can interfere with this determination.

This method requires approximately 1 hour for complete analysis, and it is suitable for industrial hygiene work. The method is not suitable for air pollution work because of the numerous interfering materials found in outside air.

Weatherburn, M. W. **Phenol-Hypochlorite Reaction for the Determination of Ammonia,** Anal. Chem. 39, 971 (1967).

Ammonia, in concentrations above 0.5 μg, can be determined by this method. The sample is collected in a fritted bubbler containing distilled water. An aliquot of the sample containing at least 0.5 μg is quantitatively transferred to a test tube. A phenol–nitroprusside solution is added, followed by the addition of alkaline hypochlorite solution. After 30 minutes the absorbance of the resulting solution is read on a spectrophotometer at a wavelength of 625 mμ.

Sampling Procedure

Collection of the sample in a fritted bubbler containing distilled water at a rate of 2.8 lpm should be adequate. At least 0.5 μg of ammonia must be collected.

The method requires approximately 1 hour for complete analysis. It is suitable for industrial hygiene work, and, if a long enough sample is collected, it should be applicable to air pollution work.

Amyl Acetate

Custance, H. M., and M. Higgins. **A Colorimetric Method for the Estimation of Amyl Acetate Vapors in the Air,** Analyst **74,** 310 (1949).

Amyl acetate, in concentrations above approximately 10 ppm, can be determined by this method. The sample is collected in two fritted bubblers connected in series, each containing 10 ml ethyl alcohol. After collection, the sample is diluted to 15 ml with ethyl alcohol, and a 2-ml aliquot is quantitatively transferred to a test tube. Sulfuric acid, water, and *p*-dimethylaminobenzaldehyde in ethyl alcohol are added and heated in a 60°C water bath for 0.5 hours. The sample is cooled and read in a spectrophotometer.

Sampling Procedure

The air sample is collected in two fritted bubblers each containing 10 ml of absolute ethanol. A sampling rate of 0.5 lpm for 30 minutes will usually collect an adequate sample.

Interferences

Butyl acetate in concentrations below approximately 1000 ppm will not significantly interfere with this determination.

Goddu, R. F., N. F. Le Blanc, and C. M. Wright. **Spectrophotometric Determination of Esters and Anhydrides by Hydroxamic Acid Reaction,** Anal. Chem. **27,** 1251 (1955).

See Also

Hill, V. T. Ind. Eng. Chem., Anal. Ed. **18,** 317 (1946).

Amyl acetate, in concentrations above approximately 20 ppm in a 25-liter air sample, can be determined by this method. The sample is collected in two fritted bubblers connected in series, each containing ethyl alcohol. It is then reacted with an alkaline hydroxylamine solution. Addition of ferric ion to this mixture produces a highly colored product. The absorbance of this product is read at a wavelength of 530 mμ. The quantity of ester present is read from a calibration curve, and the airborne concentration is calculated.

Sampling Procedure

The air sample is collected in two fritted bubblers connected in series, each containing 10 ml ethyl alcohol. The sampling rate should be approximately 1–2 lpm until at least 25 liters of air have been sampled.

Interferences

Any other ester, anhydrides, aldehydes, and isocyanates will interfere with this determination.

Analysis requires approximately 2 hours to complete. This method is applicable to industrial hygiene work but is not sufficiently sensitive for air pollution work.

Amyl Alcohol

Jacobs, Morris B. *The Analytical Chemistry of Industrial Poisons, Hazards and Solvents,* 2nd ed. (New York: Interscience Publishers, Inc., 1949), p 631.

See Also

Penniman, W. B. D., D. C. Smith, and E. I. Lawshe.   Ind. Eng. Chem., Anal. Ed. **9,** 91 (1937).

Amyl alcohol, in the parts per million range, can be determined by this method. The air sample is collected in a fritted bubbler containing distilled water. A sampling rate of 2 lpm for 30 minutes or for a period sufficient to collect a large enough sample based on an estimate of the concentration present will be adequate. A 2-ml aliquot of the sample is quantitatively transferred to a flask along with 20 ml of sulfuric acid. Salicylaldehyde or *p*-dimethylaminobenzaldehyde reagent is added and the mixture is heated. Additional sulfuric acid is added, and the color produced is compared with standards in a colorimeter.

Interferences

Other unsaturated hydrocarbons may interfere with the determination.

Amylamine

Scherberger, R. F., F. H. Miller, and D. W. Fasset. **The Determination of *n*-Butylamine in Air,** Am. Ind. Hyg. Assoc. J. **21,** 471 (1960).

Amylamine, in concentrations above 0.1 ppm in a 1-cubic foot air sample, can be determined by this method. The air sample is collected in a gas washing bottle or midget fritted bubbler containing a solution of concentrated hydrochloric acid and isopropyl alcohol. An aliquot of less than 3 ml is used for analysis. Pyridine and ninhydrin in isopropyl alcohol are added to the sample which is then heated in a water bath for 7 minutes. The sample is next cooled for 10 minutes in a cold water bath. The absorbance of the resulting solution is read in a spectrophotometer at 575 mμ. The concentration of amylamine in the sample is determined from a calibration curve and the airborne concentration calculated.

Sampling Procedure

A sampling rate of 0.1 cfm for periods ranging upwards of 10 minutes is satisfactory for collection of the amine if a fritted midget bubbler is used.

Interferences

The method is not specific for any one amine, and other amines will interfere.

The determination is simple and rapid, requiring approximately 2 hours for completion. The method is applicable to industrial hygiene work and in some cases to air pollution analysis.

Aniline

Elvove, E. **A Method for the Colorimetric Estimation of Small Amounts of Aniline,** Ind. Eng. Chem. **9,** 953 (1917).

Aniline, in concentrations above approximately 0.5 ppm, can be determined by this method. The sample is collected in a fritted bubbler at a rate of 2 lpm for a duration depending on the concentration expected. The sample is reacted with calcium hypochlorite solution and sodium hydroxide in a Nessler tube. The resulting yellow color is compared with a series of standards and the airborne concentration calculated.

The method requires approximately 30 minutes to complete the analysis. This technique is suitable for industrial hygiene work.

Jacobs, Morris B. *The Analytical Chemistry of Industrial Poisons, Hazards and Solvents,* 2nd ed. (New York: Interscience Publishers, Inc., 1949), p 710.

See Also
Elvove, E.   Ind. Eng. Chem. **9**, 953 (1917).

Aniline, in the parts per million range, can be determined by this method. The sample can be collected in a fritted bubbler containing a dilute sulfuric acid solution. After collecting the sample, calcium hypochlorite solution is added to provide an available chlorine content of 0.1%. Sodium hydroxide is then added and the purple-violet color produced compared with a set of standards. The airborne concentration of aniline is calculated.

Sampling Procedure

The sample is collected in a midget impinger containing a dilute sulfuric acid solution at a rate of 2 lpm. A 30-minute sample should provide a sufficient sample.

Interferences

Other aromatic amines may interfere with this determination.

Complete analysis requires approximately 1 hour. This method is suitable for industrial hygiene work, and if a larger sample volume is used, the method can also be used in air pollution analysis.

Riehl, W. A., and K. F. Hager.   **Rapid Detection of Aniline Vapors in Air,** Anal. Chem. **27**, 1768 (1955).

Aniline vapor, in the concentration range of 5–150 ppm, can be determined by this method. The method involves the preparation of test papers sensitive to aniline. The paper is impregnated with a furfural–acetic acid mixture. In the presence of aniline, the paper turns from white to pink or red.

Elkins, H. B. *The Chemistry of Industrial Toxicology,* 2nd ed. (New York: John Wiley and Sons, Inc., 1959), p 293.

Aniline, in concentrations above 0.1 ppm in a 50-liter air sample, can be determined by this method. The sample is collected in a gas washing bottle containing a dilute sulfuric acid solution. After collection, the sample is quantitatively transferred to a volumetric flask and diluted to 100 ml with dilute acid. A 25-ml aliquot of the sample is then transferred to an Erlenmeyer flask, and sodium bicarbonate and 1-amino-8-naphthol-3,6-disulfonic acid are added. The transmission is read on a spectrophotometer equipped with a 53 filter. The quantity of aniline present is read from a calibration curve, and the airborne concentration is calculated.

Sampling Procedure

The sample may be collected in a gas washing bottle containing sulfuric acid solution. A sampling rate of 5–10 lpm is adequate and a sample of at least 50 liters should be collected.

Analysis requires less than 1 hour to complete, and this method is suitable for industrial hygiene work.

Clipson, J. L., and L. C. Thomas. **A Field Test for Aniline Vapour in Air,** Analyst **88,** 971 (1963).

Aniline, in concentrations above 1 ppm, can be determined by this method. The sample is collected in a fritted bubbler containing 5 ml of a 5% hydrochloric acid solution. After collection, a 5-ml aliquot is transferred to a test tube, and sodium nitrite, sodium carbonate, 2-naphthal-3,6-disulfonic acid buffered to a pH of 7.5–8.5, and ammonia are added to the sample. The resulting blue color is compared with a set of standards, and the aniline concentration is calculated.

Sampling Procedure

A 6-liter sample collected at the rate of 1.5 lpm will provide an adequate sample.

The method requires approximately 1 hour for complete analysis. It is applicable to industrial hygiene work but is not sufficiently sensitive for air pollution work.

Hanson, N. W., D. A. Reilly, and H. E. Stagg, Eds. *The Determination of Toxic Substances in Air* (Cambridge, England: W. Heffer and Sons, Ltd., 1965), p 60.

Aniline, in concentrations ranging from 3–25 ppm, in a 2.5-liter sample, can be determined quickly and easily by this method. The air sample is collected in an impinger containing a dilute solution of hydrochloric acid. The sample is transferred quantitatively to a test tube and sodium hypochlorite solution is added. After 5 minutes the solution is brought to a boil. Phenol in ammonium hydroxide is added, and after 10 minutes the color is compared with a series of color standards, and the airborne concentration is calculated.

Sampling Procedure

The sampling rate through the impinger is about 0.75 lpm for periods longer than 3 minutes.

Interferences

The method is not specific for aniline. Also some of the other aromatic primary amines will interfere.

The method is simple and rapid, requiring 30 minutes for completion. No special or expensive equipment is required and the method is suitable for industrial hygiene work. This method is not considered sensitive enough for air pollution work.

Hanson, N. W., D. A. Reilly, and H. E. Stagg, Eds. *The Determination of Toxic Substances in Air* (Cambridge, England: W. Heffer and Sons, Ltd., 1965), p 56.

Aniline, in concentrations above 1 μg per 10 ml of hydrochloric acid sampling solution, can be determined quickly and easily by this method. The sample is collected in a fritted bubbler containing 10 ml of a standardized hydrochloric acid solution. The sample is quantitatively transferred to a volumetric flask. A sodium nitrite solution is added and allowed to stand for 15 minutes at a temperature below 15°C. Sodium sulphamate, sodium acetate, N-sulphatoethyl-*m*-toluidine and hydrochloric acid are added. Ten minutes is required for full color development. The optical density of the solution is read on a spectrophotometer at a wavelength of 500 mμ. The quantity of aniline present is determined from a previously prepared calibration curve, and the airborne concentration is calculated.

The sampling rate through the fritted bubbler should be approximately 5 lpm. The duration of sampling depends on the expected concentration of the amine.

Interferences

Many amines and their derivatives interfere with this method.

The method is relatively simple and requires about 2 hours for complete analysis. No special or expensive equipment is required. This method is suitable for industrial hygiene work.

Hanson, N. W., D. A. Reilly, and H. E. Stagg, Eds. *The Determination of Toxic Substances in Air* (Cambridge, England: W. Heffer and Sons, Ltd., 1965), p 63.

Aniline, in concentrations ranging from 1.5–15 ppm in a 0.5-liter sample, can be determined quickly and easily by this method. The air sample is collected in a midget impinger containing 10 ml diluted hydrochloric acid. Methyl orange indicator is added to the sample which is then neutralized with sodium hydroxide. The sample is lightly acidified with hydrochloric acid, after which sodium hypochlorite solution is added. After 5 minutes the excess hypochlorite is removed by adding sodium thiosulfate. A solution of phenol in sodium hydroxide is added to the sample and after dilution with water the solution is allowed to stand for 20 minutes. The optical density of the resulting blue solution is read at a wavelength of 620 mμ. The quantity of aniline is read from a previously prepared calibration curve, and the airborne concentration is calculated.

Sampling Procedure

The sampling rate through the impinger should be 0.5–0.75 lpm. The duration of sampling will depend upon the expected concentration. A sampling duration ranging from 1–10 minutes will usually cover all cases.

Interferences

The method is not specific for aniline, and some of the other aromatic primary amines may interfere.

The method is simple and requires approximately 1.5 hours for complete analysis. No special or expensive equipment is required, and the method is suitable for industrial hygiene work. This method is not considered to be sensitive enough for general air pollution work, but it is suitable for stack sampling applications.

Hong, W. H., and K. A. Conners. **Spectrophotometric Determination of Aliphatic Amines by Acylation with Cinnamic Anhydride**, Anal. Chem. **40**, 1273 (1968).

Aniline, in concentrations at the parts per million level, can be determined by this method. This method was not designed specifically for air analysis but appears to be applicable. A 1-ml aliquot of the sample is quantitatively transferred to a 50-ml volumetric flask. Cinnamic anhydride solution and tri-*n*-butylamine in acetonitrile are added, mixed and allowed to react at room temperature for several minutes. Sodium hydroxide is added to the 50-ml mark and allowed to stand for 10 minutes. The sample mixture is quantitatively transferred to a separatory funnel and extracted with chloroform. The chloroform extract is washed with distilled water and filtered into a 50-ml volumetric flask. The sample is made to volume with chloroform, and the absorbance of the sample is read in a spectrophotometer at 295 mμ. The airborne concentration of aniline is calculated.

Sampling Procedure

An air sampling procedure must be developed. Collection might be accomplished using a fritted bubbler containing an acetonitrile solution.

Interferences

Any aliphatic amine will interfere with this method.

Stewart, J. T., T. D. Shaw, and A. B. Ray. **Spectrophotometric Determination of Primary Aromatic Amines with 9-Chloroacridine,** Anal. Chem. **41,** 360 (1969).

This method was not designed for air analysis but appears to be modifiable for this use. Most of these amines have some vapor pressure; therefore, this analysis is abstracted here.

Aniline in concentrations above approximately 10^{-7} moles can be determined by this method. The sample can probably be collected in ethyl alcohol. After collection, a 1-ml aliquot of the amine is quantitatively transferred to a volumetric flask. A solution of 9-chloroacridine is added and the pH is adjusted to 4.0 with hydrochloric acid. The absorbance of the resulting orange-colored solution is read on a spectrophotometer at 435 mμ.

Sampling Procedure

The sample may be collected in a fritted bubbler at a rate of 2 lpm.

Interferences

Primary amines and acridine will interfere with this determination.

The method requires approximately 1 hour for complete analysis. It is suitable for industrial hygiene work.

Arsenic

Oliver, W. T., and H. S. Funnell. **Determination of Arsenic in Biological Material,** Anal. Chem. 31, 259 (1959).

The method as described is utilized for the determination of arsenic, but during the course of the determination the arsenic is converted to arsine; therefore, the method can be modified for use in the determination of arsine.

The arsine in the air sample should be absorbable on mercuric iodide crystals contained in a U-tube. The arsine is then eluted with iodine solution and reacted with molybdate reagent and hydrazine sulfate solution at the temperature of boiling water. The resulting blue color is read at 720 mμ in a spectrophotometer and the quantity present is determined from a standard curve. The airborne concentration is then calculated.

A sampling rate of about 1 lpm should be satisfactory. Sensitivity and interferences require further investigation when the method is used for the airborne determination of arsine.

The method requires approximately 1.5 hours for complete analysis. It is suitable for industrial hygiene work.

Azulene

Sawicki, E., T. W. Stanley, and W. C. Elbert. **Spot Test Detection and Spectrophotometric Determination of Azulene Derivatives with 4-Dimethylaminobenzaldehyde,** Anal. Chem. 33, 1183 (1961).

Azulene can be determined in concentrations as low as one part azulene in five million parts of sample solution.

No data were presented on collection methods but it appears that a sample could be collected in ethyl or methyl alcohol. A solution of 4-dimethylaminobenzaldehyde in acetic acid is added to the alcoholic sample. Hydrochloric acid and trichloroacetic acid are added and the resulting blue color is allowed to develop for 15 minutes. The absorbance is read in a spectrophotometer at 620 mμ and compared with a standard curve.

No information on sampling rates is given but 1 cfm through a Greenburg-Smith impinger containing 75–100 ml alcohol appears to be reasonable.

Interferences

Other azulene compounds will interfere. Pyrroles and indoles are the other main possible interferences.

The method is sufficiently sensitive to be used for air analysis. Analysis requires about 30 minutes.

Benzaldehyde

Ruch, J. E., and J. B. Johnson. **Determination of Aldehydes by Mercurimetric Oxidation,** Anal. Chem. **28,** 69 (1956).

Benzaldehyde, in the parts per million range, can be determined by this method. It is not designed for air analysis and a sampling procedure must be devised. The sample is quantitatively transferred to an Erlenmeyer flask and 50 ml of a solution of potassium iodide in potassium hydroxide are added. The sample is kept cool in an ice bath; then 50 ml of agar and 25 ml of glacial acetic acid are added. A standardized iodine solution is added and after 15 minutes the sample is titrated with standardized thiosulfate solution. The quantity of aldehyde present is then calculated.

Sampling Procedure

No air sampling procedure has yet been developed.

Interferences

Alcohol and esters interfere slightly with this determination. Some vinyl compounds, unsaturated aldehydes, acetone and methyl ethyl ketone also interfere slightly.

Benzene

Dolin, B. H. **Determination of Benzene in Presence of Toluene, Xylene and Other Substances,** Ind. Eng. Chem., Anal. Ed. **15,** 242 (1943).

See Also
1. Jacobs, Morris B. *The Chemical Analysis of Air Pollutants* (New York: Interscience Publishers, Inc., 1960), p 256.
2. Schrenk, H. H., S. J. Pearce, and W. P. Yant. U.S. Bur. Mines, Rept. Invest. **3287** (1935).
3. Pearce, S. J., H. H. Schrenk, and W. P. Yant. U.S. Bur. Mines, Rept. Invest. **3302** (1936).
4. Dolin, B. H. Ind. Eng. Chem., Anal. Ed. **15**, 242 (1943).
5. Dolin, B. H. N.Y. State Ind. Bull. **25**, #7 (1946).

Benzene, in concentrations above 0.5–1 ppm, can be determined by this method if 5 liters of air are sampled. The air sample is collected in petroleum naphtha or alcohol in a fritted bubbler. An aliquot of the sample is cooled to 0° to −5°C in an acid and salt bath. Nitrating acid, consisting of equal volumes of concentrated nitric and sulfuric acid, is added to the sample. After diluting with distilled water the sample is cooled to room temperature and the nitrated materials extracted with ether. The ether extract is washed with sodium hydroxide and water; it is then diluted with ethyl alcohol. Butanone and alcoholic sodium hydroxide are added to an aliquot of the above sample and the colors produced are observed. Acetic acid is added to the sample; colors due to xylene and toluene are destroyed while the crimson color produced by benzene remains unaltered. The crimson color is read in a spectrophotometer at 620 mμ and the quantity of benzene present is read from a calibration curve.

The sampling rate can be maintained at about 0.5 lpm through the fritted bubbler.

Interferences

Toluene and xylene do not interfere. The method appears to be relatively specific for benzene.

The method can be applied to industrial hygiene analysis and apparently is sufficiently sensitive for air pollution work. The method requires about 30 minutes for completion.

Jacobs, Morris B. *The Analytical Chemistry of Industrial Poisons, Hazards and Solvents*, 2nd ed. (New York: Interscience Publishers, Inc., 1949), p 527.

See Also
1. Schrenk, H. H., S. J. Pearce, and W. P. Yant. U.S. Bur. Mines, Rept. Invest. **3287** (1935).
2. Pearce, S. J., H. H. Schrenk, and W. P. Yant. U.S. Bur. Mines, Rept. Invest. **3302** (1936).

Benzene, in concentrations above approximately 25 ppm, can be determined by this method if a 0.5-liter air sample is collected. This limit can be extended by increasing the sampling time significantly. The air sample is collected through a special bubbler containing a nitrating acid composed of equal parts of concentrated sulfuric acid and fuming nitric acid. After collection, the sample is allowed to react for 30 minutes to insure complete nitration. The sample is quantitatively transferred to an Erlenmeyer flask, cooled below 20°C, and then neutralized by adding sodium hydroxide slowly and carefully. This solution is warmed to 30°C, and 10 ml of methyl ethyl ketone (butanone) are added. The sample is transferred to a separatory funnel and the water drawn off. Sodium hydroxide is added and the color is allowed to develop for 1 hour. The resulting violet color is compared with a set of standards and the quantity present in the sample is determined. The airborne concentration is calculated.

Sampling Procedure

The sample may be collected in a special bubbler containing nitrating acid. A sampling rate of 30 ml per minute for approximately 1 hour should provide a sufficient sample for analysis.

Interferences

Toluene, ethylbenzene, chlorobenzene, styrene, and xylene will interfere with this determination.

Analysis requires approximately 3 hours. If a 60-minute sample is collected, the method is suitable for industrial hygiene work but is not sufficiently sensitive for air pollution work.

Moffett, P. A., T. F. Doherty, and J. L. Monkman. **Collection and Determination of Microamounts of Benzene or Toluene in Air,** Am. Ind. Hyg. Assoc. Quart. **17,** 186 (1956).

Benzene in quantities greater than about 0.5 mg can be determined by this method. The sample is collected by drawing the air through a tube containing silica gel. After collection the gel is immersed in iso-octane, and water is added. The water displaces the aromatic hydrocarbon which dissolves in the iso-octane. The absorbance is determined at 254.5 mμ in a spectrophotometer and the quantity present is determined directly from a calibration curve.

Sampling Procedure

The sample can be collected at a rate of 1 cfm for a period dictated by the concentration expected.

Interferences

Benzene must be the only hydrocarbon present because many other hydrocarbons will interfere.

The method is applicable to industrial hygiene work and requires less than 1 hour for analysis.

Elkins, H. B., L. D. Pagnotto, and E. M. Comprone. **The Ultraviolet Determination of Benzene in Air Samples Adsorbed on Silica Gel,** Anal. Chem. **34,** 1797 (1962).

Benzene, in concentrations exceeding 10 ppm, can be determined by this procedure.

The air sample is collected on silica gel contained in a U-tube. If other aromatics are known to be absent, the sample is extracted from the silica gel with 50 ml of isopropyl alcohol. After standing for at least 2 hours, the absorbance in the range of 240–280 mμ is determined. The quantity of benzene present in the sample is read from a calibration curve.

Sampling Procedure

The sampling rate is 1–3 lpm until a total of 50 liters is collected.

Interferences

Other aromatic hydrocarbons will interfere.

This method is applicable to industrial hygiene work and to determination of stack concentrations. It is not suitable for air pollution work.

Dambrauskas, T., and W. A. Cook. **Methanol as the Absorbing Reagent in the Determination of Benzene, Toluene, Xylene and Their Mixtures in Air,** Am. Ind. Hyg. Assoc. J. **24,** 568 (1963).

Benzene, toluene, xylene and their mixtures can be determined in the parts per million range. The sample is collected in a gas washing bottle immersed in dry ice. The absorbing solution used is methanol. A rate of 1 lpm for 30 minutes usually will collect a suitable sample. After collection, the absorbances of benzene at a wavelength of 254.5 mμ, toluene at a wavelength of 268.5 mμ and xylene at a wavelength of 272.0 mμ are determined. A set of standards is prepared and the concentration of each component in the mixture calculated.

Sampling Procedure

A gas washing bottle containing 50 ml of methanol is used to collect the sample. A sampling rate of 1 lpm for 30 minutes will usually provide a suitable sample.

Interferences

Any material absorbing at the wavelength of interest will interfere with the determination. The method is suitable for industrial hygiene work where concentrations are above 10 ppm. The method is not sufficiently sensitive for air pollution work and requires about 1 hour for complete analysis.

Hanson, N. W., D. A. Reilly, and H. E. Stagg, Eds. *The Determination of Toxic Substances in Air* (Cambridge, England: W. Heffer and Sons, Ltd., 1965), p 51.

Benzene, in concentrations ranging from 10–100 ppm in a 0.25-liter sample, can be determined quickly and easily by this method. Increasing or decreasing the air sample volume will increase or decrease the concentration range to which the method is applicable. The sample is collected in a special U-tube containing a solution of formaldehyde and sulfuric acid. After collection, the sample is quantitatively transferred to a 25-ml volumetric flask and diluted to the mark with the formaldehyde–sulfuric acid reagent. The optical density of the color produced is read in a spectrophotometer at 445 mμ. The concentration in the sample is read from a calibration curve, and the airborne concentration of benzene is calculated.

The sampling rate through the U-tube containing the formaldehyde–sulfuric acid solution should be about 50-ml per minute for a period sufficient to collect about 250 ml.

Interferences

The method is not specific for benzene and any aromatic hydrocarbon will interfere with this determination.

The method is simple and rapid, requiring about 1.5 hours for complete analysis. No expensive equipment is required. This method is suitable for industrial hygiene work but is not sufficiently sensitive for air pollution work.

Benzylamine

Hong, W. H., and K. A. Conners. **Spectrophotometric Determination of Aliphatic Amines by Acylation with Cinnamic Anhydride,** Anal. Chem. **40,** 1273 (1968).

Benzylamine, in concentrations at the parts per million level, can be determined by this method. This method was not designed specifically for air analysis but appears to be applicable. A 1-ml aliquot of the sample is quantitatively transferred to a 50-ml volumetric flask. Cinnamic anhydride solution and tri-*n*-butylamine in acetonitrile are added, mixed and allowed to react at room temperature for several minutes. Sodium hydroxide is added to the 50-ml mark and allowed to stand for 10 minutes. The sample mixture is quantitatively transferred to a separatory funnel and extracted with chloroform. The chloroform extract is washed with distilled water and filtered into a 50-ml volumetric flask. The sample is made to volume with chloroform and the absorbance of the sample is read in a spectrophotometer at 275 mμ. The airborne concentration of benzylamine is calculated.

Sampling Procedure

An air sampling procedure must be developed. Collection might be accomplished using a fritted bubbler containing an acetonitrile solution.

Interferences

Any aliphatic amine will interfere with this method.

Bromine

Elkins, H. B. *The Chemistry of Industrial Toxicology,* 2nd ed. (New York: John Wiley and Sons, Inc., 1958), p 305.

Bromine, in concentrations above 0.2 ppm, can be determined by this method if a 5-l air sample is collected. The sample is collected in a midget impinger containing a solution of *o*-tolidine in hydrochloric acid. The yellow color produced is visually compared with a set of standards prepared from potassium dichromate, and the airborne concentration is calculated.

Sampling Procedure

The sample may be collected in a midget impinger containing o-tolidine reagent. A sampling rate of 1 lpm for 5 minutes should provide a sample suitable for analysis. No more than 5 liters of air may be sampled.

Interferences

The method is not specific for bromine, and any oxidizing agent or reducing material will interfere.

The method is suitable for industrial hygiene work but is not sufficiently sensitive for air pollution work. Analysis can be completed in approximately 30 minutes.

Hanson, N. W., D. A. Reilly, and H. E. Stagg, Eds. *The Determination of Toxic Substances in Air* (Cambridge, England: W. Heffer and Sons, Ltd., 1965), p 81.

Bromine, in concentrations ranging from 0.1–2.0 or 1.0–10.0 ppm, can be determined quickly and easily by this method. The air sample is drawn through a filter paper impregnated with eosin or eosin and sodium fluorescein until the color developed matches one of the two color standards. Knowing the volume of air required to produce the pink color matching the standards, one can calculate the concentration of bromine.

The sampling rate through the impregnated paper should be about 0.8 lpm until the color of the sample matches the color of one of the standards.

The method is simple and rapid, requiring only a few minutes to complete the analysis. It is suitable for industrial hygiene work.

Jacobs, Morris B. *The Analytical Toxicology of Industrial Inorganic Poisons* (New York: Interscience Publishers, Inc., 1967), p 656.

Bromine vapor at concentrations above approximately 0.5 ppm can be determined by this method. The sample is collected in a gas washing bottle containing a potassium hydroxide solution. The sampling rate should be 2 lpm and a 30-liter sample should be collected. After collection, the sample is reacted with hydrogen peroxide and determined as silver bromide.

Larsen, R. P., and N. M. Ingber. **Determination of Bromine in Uranium Fluorides and Oxides,** Anal. Chem. **31,** 1084 (1959).

Bromine and bromides in concentration down to 0.1 ppm can be determined by this method. The method as described is not a method for air analysis but should be applicable to this type of procedure.

The sample can be collected in water using a midget impinger or a bubbler. The sample is then added to a chromic–sulfuric acid solution. When bromide is oxidized to bromine, the bromine is distilled into a few milliliters of sodium sulfite solution. The bromine is extracted with carbon tetrachloride and stripped from the carbon tetrachloride with ammonium hydroxide. Sodium hydroxide is added and the solution is evaporated to dryness. The resulting salt is dissolved in water, acidified with sulfuric acid, and buffered with borate. Calcium hypochlorite and phenol red reagent are added, and the bromination of the phenol red is continued for 4 minutes. It is then stopped with sodium arsenite and buffered with acetate. The absorbance is read at 590 mμ. Standards are prepared from known bromide solutions. Sampling rates of 0.1 lpm should be satisfactory.

Interferences

Bromides interfere.

The method is quantitative for bromine concentrations down to 0.1 ppm assuming a sufficiently large volume of air is sampled.

p-Bromoaniline

Stewart, J. T., T. D. Shaw, and A. B. Ray. **Spectrophotometric Determination of Primary Aromatic Amines with 9-Chloroacridine.** Anal. Chem. **41,** 360 (1969).

This method was not designed for air analysis but appears to be modifiable for this use. Most of these amines have some vapor pressure; therefore, this analysis is abstracted here.

p-Bromoaniline in concentrations above approximately 10^{-7} moles can be determined by this method. The sample can be collected in ethyl alcohol. After collection, a 1-ml aliquot of the amine is quantitatively transferred to a volumetric flask. A solution of 9-chloroacridine is added and the pH is adjusted to 4.0 with hydrochloric acid. The absorbance of the resulting orange-colored solution is read in a spectrophotometer at 435 mμ.

Sampling Procedure

The sample is collected in a fritted bubbler at a rate of 2 lpm.

Interferences

Primary amines and acridine will interfere with this determination. Complete analysis requires approximately 1 hour. This method is suitable for industrial hygiene work.

Bromoform

Jacobs, M. B. *The Analytical Chemistry of Industrial Poisons, Hazards and Solvents,* 2nd ed. (New York: Interscience Publishers, Inc., 1949), p 565.

See Also

1. Cole, W. H.   J. Biol. Chem. **71,** 173 (1926).
2. Gettler, A. O., and H. Blume.   Arch. Pathol. **11,** 555 (1931).
3. Ross, J. H.   J. Biol. Chem. **58,** 641 (1923/24).

Bromoform in the parts per million range can be determined by this method. The air sample is collected in a bubbler containing 95% ethyl alcohol. After collection, the sample is quantitatively transferred to a volumetric flask and diluted to volume. Pyridine, sodium hydroxide, and an aliquot of the sample are placed in a test tube and heated in a water bath for 1 minute. The resulting color in the pyridine layer is compared with a set of color standards in a color comparator. The permanent color standards are prepared from basic fuchsin in acidified ethyl alcohol. The concentration of bromoform in air is calculated.

Sampling Procedure

The air sample is collected in a bubbler containing either dilute hydrochloric acid or ethyl alcohol. A sampling rate of 2 lpm for at least 30 minutes should provide an adequate sample.

Interferences

Any material with a 3 halogen-carbon linkage will interfere with this determination. Examples of such compounds are bromoform, iodoform, Chloretone, and chloral.

The method requires approximately 1 hour for complete analysis. It is applicable to industrial hygiene work but is not sufficiently sensitive for air pollution analysis.

2-Butanone

Hashmi, M. H., and A. A. Ayaz.   **The Determination of Methyl Ke-tones and Acetaldehydes by Titration with Hypobromite Using Bor-deaux Indicator,** Anal. Chem. **36,** 385 (1964).

2-Butanone can be simply, accurately and rapidly determined with this method. The method, although not designed for air analysis, should be applicable with some modification. The sample could be collected in water using an impinger or a fritted bubbler. A measured aliquot of sample is placed in a flask, 3N sodium hydroxide is added, and the mixture is titrated against standard hypobromite solution using Bordeaux as an internal indicator. The end point shows up as a change from light pink to faint yellow or colorless.

A sampling rate of about 1–2 lpm should be adequate for collection of the sample.

Interferences

Aliphatic aldehydes and methyl ketones will interfere, as will high concentrations of aldehydes.

The method should have application in ambient air, industrial hy-giene, and stack gas analysis. Analysis should require less than 1 hour to complete.

n-Butyl Acetate

Goddu, R. F., N. F. Le Blanc, and C. M. Wright.   **Spectrophotometric Determination of Esters and Anhydrides by Hydroxamic Acid Re-action,** Anal. Chem. **27,** 1251 (1955).

See Also

Hill, V. T.   Ind. Eng. Chem., Anal. Ed. **18,** 317 (1946).

n-Butyl acetate, in concentrations above approximately 20 ppm in a 25-liter air sample, can be determined by this method. The sample is collected in two fritted bubblers connected in series, each containing ethyl alcohol. The sample is reacted with an alkaline hydroxylamine solution. The addition of ferric ion to this mixture produces a highly colored product. The absorbance of this product is read at a wavelength of 530 mμ. The quantity of ester present is read from a calibration curve, and the airborne concentration is calculated.

Sampling Procedure

The air sample may be collected in two fritted bubblers connected in series, each containing 10 ml ethyl alcohol. The sampling rate should be approximately 1–2 lpm until at least 25 liters of air have been sampled.

Interferences

Any other ester, anhydrides, aldehydes, and isocyanates will interfere with this determination.

This method requires approximately 2 hours for complete analysis. It is applicable to industrial hygiene work but is not sufficiently sensitive for air pollution work.

Hanson, N. W., D. A. Reilly, and H. E. Stagg, Eds.   *The Determination of Toxic Substances in Air* (Cambridge, England: W. Heffer and Sons, Ltd., 1965), p 37.

See Also

Hestrin, S. J.   J. Biol. Chem. **180,** 249 (1949).

Butyl acetate, in concentrations ranging from 10–400 ppm, can be determined quickly and accurately by this method. The sample is collected in an impinger containing ethyl alcohol. The sample is quantitatively transferred to a volumetric flask and a solution of hydroxylammonium chloride is added. Following this, sodium hydroxide, hydrochloric acid, and ferric chloride are added. The sample is then diluted to 25 ml with water and allowed to stand for 30 minutes. The optical density of the resulting purple solution is read in a spectrophotometer at 510 mμ.

The sampling rate should be approximately 0.5 lpm. Approximately 0.6 liters of air should be sampled to provide the sensitivity stated above. Increasing or decreasing the volume of air sampled will increase or decrease the concentration range to which this method is applicable.

Interferences

Methyl, ethyl, and isoamyl acetate will interfere with this analysis. The anhydrides and chlorides of carboxylic acids also interfere.

The method is simple, requires approximately 1.5 hours to complete, and requires no special or expensive equipment. It is suitable for industrial hygiene work but is not sufficiently sensitive for air pollution work.

Butyl Alcohol

Elkins, H. B. *The Chemistry of Industrial Toxicology*, 2nd ed. (New York: John Wiley and Sons, 1959), p 306.

Butyl alcohol, in concentrations above 5 ppm, can be determined by this method if a 25-liter air sample is collected. The sample is collected in two Petri bubblers, each containing 20 ml of distilled water. After collection, the sample is refluxed for 1 hour and cooled. Potassium iodide is added, and the mixture is titrated with sodium thiosulfate. The airborne concentration of butyl alcohol is calculated.

Sampling Procedure

The sample is collected in two Petri bubblers connected in series. A sampling rate of 1–2 lpm for 30 minutes will usually collect an adequate sample.

Interferences

Water soluble alcohols and some other water soluble organic compounds will interfere with this determination.

This method is suitable for industrial hygiene work but is not sufficiently sensitive for air pollution work. Complete analysis requires approximately 2.5 hours.

Hoare, D. E., and R. R. Ogilvie. **Spectrophotometric Method for the Microdetermination of Monohydric Aliphatic Alcohols,** Anal. Chem. **38,** 1799 (1966).

This method was not designed for air analysis but appears to be applicable for this use. Butyl alcohol in concentrations in excess of 0.1 μg per ml can be determined by this method. The sample is collected in a midget impinger containing water. An 8-ml aliquot of the sample, an acetate buffer, and a sodium nitrite solution are quantitatively transferred to a 50-ml flask. The sample is incubated at 18°C for 30 minutes after which heptane is added. The sample is incubated again at 18°C and agitated. It is cooled to 0°C and transferred to a cold separatory funnel; the aqueous layer is removed. The heptane layer is transferred to a test tube and exposed to calcium chloride to remove water. The sample is reacted with α-naphthylamine and incubated at 18°C for 10 minutes. The color is allowed to develop while the sample is contained in a water bath at 60°C for 30 minutes. After cooling, the absorbance of the resulting solution is read in a spectrophotometer at 550 mμ. The concentration present in the sample is read from a calibration curve; and the airborne concentration is calculated.

Sampling Procedure

The sample is collected by a fritted bubbler at a rate of 2 lpm. Water may be used as the sampling solution.

Interferences

The method is not specific for monohydric aliphatic alcohols but determines many of them.

Complete analysis requires approximately 3 hours. This method is suitable for industrial hygiene work.

Butylamine

Scherberger, R. F., F. H. Miller, and D. W. Fasset. **The Determination of *n*-Butylamine in Air,** Am. Ind. Hyg. Assoc. J. **21,** 471 (1960).

n-Butylamine, in concentrations above 0.1 ppm in a 1-cubic foot air sample, can be determined by this method. The air sample is collected in a gas washing bottle or midget fritted bubbler containing a solution of concentrated hydrochloric acid and isopropyl alcohol. An aliquot of less than 3 ml is used for analysis. Pyridine and ninhydrin in isopropyl alcohol are added to the sample which is then heated in a water bath for 7 minutes. The sample is next cooled for 10 minutes in a cold water bath. The absorbance of the resulting solution is read in a spectrophotometer at 575 mμ. The concentration of butylamine in the sample is determined from a calibration curve, and the airborne concentration is calculated.

Sampling Procedure

A sampling rate of 0.1 cfm for periods ranging upwards of 10 minutes is satisfactory for collection of the amine if a fritted midget bubbler is used.

Interferences

The method is not specific for any one amine and other amines will interfere.

The determination is simple and rapid, requiring approximately 2 hours for completion. This method is applicable to industrial hygiene work and in some cases to air pollution analysis.

Hong, W. H., and K. A. Conners. **Spectrophotometric Determination of Aliphatic Amines by Acylation with Cinnamic Anhydride,** Anal. Chem. **40,** 1273 (1968).

n-Butylamine, in concentrations at the parts per million level, can be determined by this method. This method was not designed specifically for air analysis but appears to be applicable. A 1-ml aliquot of the sample is quantitatively transferred to a 50-ml volumetric flask. Cinnamic anhydride solution and tri-n-butylamine in acetonitrile are added, mixed and allowed to react at room temperature for several minutes. Sodium hydroxide is added to the 50-ml mark and the sample is allowed to stand for 10 minutes. It is quantitatively transferred to a separatory funnel and extracted with chloroform. The chloroform extract is washed with distilled water and filtered into a 50-ml volumetric flask. The sample is made to volume with chloroform and the absorbance of the sample is read in a spectrophotometer at 274 mμ. The airborne concentration of n-butylamine is calculated.

Sampling Procedure

An air sampling procedure must be developed. Collection might be accomplished using a fritted bubbler containing an acetonitrile solution.

Interferences

Any aliphatic amine will interfere with this method.

n-Butyl Mercaptan

Turk, E., and E. E. Reid. **Copper Alkyl Phthalates for the Estimation of Mercaptans,** Ind. Eng. Chem., Anal. Ed. **17,** 713 (1945).

n-Butyl mercaptans, in concentrations above 40 mg per sample, can be determined by this method. Although the method needs to be tested for air analysis, it appears to have application in certain areas of air pollution work. The sample might be collected in an alcohol solvent using a standard impinger. After collection, the sample is titrated with copper butyl phthalate to a persistent blue-green end point.

A sampling rate of up to 1 cfm through the standard impinger containing 75–100 ml alcohol should be satisfactory.

Interferences

Hydrogen sulfide interferes with the determination; if this gas is present the method cannot be used. The method determines total mercaptans.

The method could be adapted for stack gas analysis but does not appear to be sufficiently sensitive for air pollution or industrial hygiene work. Analysis requires less than 1 hour for completion.

Moore, H., H. L. Helwig, and R. J. Grave. **A Spectrophotometer Method for the Determination of Mercaptans in Air,** Am. Ind. Hyg. J. **21**, 466 (1960).

Butyl mercaptan, in concentrations above 0.5 ppm in a 1-liter air sample, can be rapidly and accurately determined by this method. The air sample is collected in a fritted bubbler containing mercuric acetate solution and is placed in a volumetric flask and diluted with distilled water. *N,N*-Dimethyl-*p*-phenylenediamine in hydrochloric acid and ferric chloride in nitric acid solution are added to the sample. The resulting red color is allowed to develop for 30 minutes and read in a spectrophotometer at 500 mμ. Standards are prepared from lead methyl mercaptide.

Sampling Procedure

Sampling rates of less than 0.5 lpm for a fritted bubbler and 1.5 lpm for a large bubbler are satisfactory for collection of the mercaptan. A 30-minute sample is usually sufficient.

Interferences

The method is not specific for any one mercaptan and all mercaptans will interfere. Hydrogen sulfide, sulfur dioxide, and nitrogen dioxide do not interfere at the concentrations usually found in air pollution or industrial hygiene studies.

The method is applicable to both industrial hygiene and air pollution work. The method requires about 2 hours for completion.

Butyraldehyde

Sawicki, E., T. R. Hauser, T. W. Stanley, and W. Elbert. **The 3-Methyl-2-Benzothiazolone Hydrozone Test. Sensitive New Methods for the Detection, Rapid Estimation and Determination of Aliphatic Aldehydes,** Anal. Chem. **33,** 93 (1961).

Butyraldehyde can be analyzed in quantities as low as 5 μg per 100 ml of solution. Butyraldehyde, and other aliphatic aldehydes, can be determined specifically if only one of these compounds is present in the contaminated air.

Air is sampled through an impinger containing a collecting solution of 10 ml of 3-methyl-2-benzothiazolone and distilled water. The solution is transferred to a volumetric flask and aqueous ferric chloride is added. The mixture is then diluted to 100 ml with acetone. The absorbance of the resulting blue color is read in a spectrophotometer at 670 mμ and the quantity of aldehyde present is read from a calibration curve.

Sampling Procedure

A sampling rate of 2 lpm through a midget impinger containing 10 ml of solution should be satisfactory for collection of the aldehyde.

Interferences

Other aliphatic aldehydes interfere. If they exist singly in the air to be sampled, they can be accurately determined by this method. Also thought to interfere are aniline, *N*-alkylanilines, *N,N*-dialkylanilines, indoles, carbozoles, and phenothiazines.

The method is quantitative for butyraldehyde from a concentration of 5–125 μg per 100 ml of solution. The method is applicable to air and auto exhaust analysis. Complete analysis requires approximately 30 minutes.

Albrecht, A. M., W. I. Scher, Jr., and H. J. Vogel. **Determination of Aliphatic Aldehydes by Spectrophotometry,** Anal. Chem. **34,** 398 (1962).

Butyraldehyde can be determined quantitatively at concentrations below 0.4 moles per ml of sampling solution.

The air sample may be collected in a midget impinger containing 10 ml of distilled water. A solution of methylamine hydrochloride in sodium pyrophosphate is added to an aliquot of this sample. Then a solution of *o*-aminobenzaldehyde is added. The absorbance of the yellow-colored reaction mixture is read at 440 mμ in a spectrophotometer. The quantity present is read from a calibration curve.

The sampling rate may be 0.1 cfm through a midget impinger or 1 cfm through a standard impinger. Scrubbers or gas washing bottles may be used. A 30-minute sampling time will usually collect a suitable sample.

Interferences

Other aliphatic aldehydes interfere and many of them can be determined by this method.   '

The method is useful for atmospheric sampling and analysis and should be adaptable for use at stack concentrations. Time required for analysis is approximately 1 hour.

Kwan, T. W., and B. M. Watts.   **A New Color Reaction of Anthrone with Malonaldehyde and Other Aliphatic Aldehydes,** Anal. Chem. **35,** 733 (1963).

A method is described for the analysis of butyraldehyde using anthrone as the color-forming reagent. The method appears to be applicable to air samples containing elevated concentrations of the aldehyde. More work needs to be done to determine sampling solution, sampling rates and sensitivities before the method can be used routinely.

Carbon Dioxide

Loveland, J. W., R. W. Adams, H. H. King, Jr., F. A. Nowak, and L. J. Cali. **Spectrophotometric Titration of Parts per Million of Carbon Dioxide in Gases,** Anal. Chem. **31,** 1008 (1959).

Carbon dioxide in the range of 1–50 ppm can be determined by this method. The sample can be collected in fritted bubblers, preferably two or more in series, containing sodium hydroxide of known normality. The sample is back-titrated with hydrochloric acid of known normality using phenolphthalein as the indicator. The titration is followed on a spectrophotometer at 555 mμ. The sampling rate should be kept low, around 100 ml per minute. The upper limit of 50 ppm can probably be extended by varying the normality of the collecting solution and titrant.

Interferences

Any acidic or basic material will interfere with the analysis. Complete analysis requires approximately 1 hour.

Hanson, N. W., D. A. Reilly, and H. E. Stagg, Eds. *The Determination of Toxic Substances in Air* (Cambridge, England: W. Heffer and Sons, Ltd., 1965), p 33.

Carbon dioxide, in concentrations ranging from 2,000–60,000 ppm in a 0.5-liter air sample, can be determined quickly and easily. The air sample is collected in a Drechsel bottle containing a mixture of sodium hydroxide and barium chloride solutions. Following collection, the sample is titrated with a standard hydrochloric acid solution using phenophthalein as the indicator. After titration, a methyl orange–xylene cyanol indicator is added along with a known excess of hydrochloric acid. The sample is then titrated with a standard sodium hydroxide solution. The difference between the two end points and the volume of air sampled is used to calculate the carbon dioxide concentration.

Interferences

Ammonia interferes with the determination, but passing the air sample through a calcium chloride solution prior to absorption in the Drechsel bottle removes this interference.

The method is simple and rapid, requiring approximately 30 minutes to complete the analysis. It is considered suitable for industrial hygiene work.

Jacobs, Morris B. *The Analytical Toxicology of Industrial Inorganic Poisons* (New York: Interscience Publishers, Inc., 1967), p 720.

Many volumetric methods are available for the determination of carbon dioxide. A known volume of gas is collected and then passed through sodium or potassium hydroxide in some type of calibrated volumetric instrument. The volume of carbon dioxide in the sample is determined from the shrinkage observed in the sample.

Jacobs, Morris B. *The Analytical Toxicology of Industrial Inorganic Poisons* (New York: Interscience Publishers, Inc., 1967), p 721.

See Also

Elkins, H. B. *The Chemistry of Industrial Toxicology*, 2nd ed. (New York: John Wiley and Sons, Inc., 1959), p 310.

The carbon dioxide air sample is collected in a bubbler containing a standardized solution of barium hydroxide. After collection, the excess barium hydroxide in the sample is titrated with a standardized oxalic acid solution using thymolphthalein as the indicator.

Carbon Disulfide

Viles, F. J. **Field Determinations of Carbon Disulfide in Air,** J. Ind. Hyg. Toxicol. **22,** 188 (1940).

Four sampling methods for collecting carbon disulfide are detailed. The analytical method used is the copper diethylamine method. The modification by McKee [J. Ind. Hyg. Toxicol. **23,** 151 (1941)] is a more suitable analytical method because of certain concentration changes applied to the collecting reagent. The McKee variation can be used with any of the sampling methods discussed.

The sampling methods described include a bubbler method, the pump absorption method, and two grab-sampling methods.

McKee, R. W. **A Quantitative Microchemical Colorimetric Determination of Carbon Disulfide in Air, Water and Biological Fluids,** J. Ind. Hyg. Toxicol. **23,** 151 (1941).

Carbon disulfide, in concentrations above 0.7 μg per aliquot analyzed, can be determined by this method. The air sample is collected in a fritted bubbler containing a 10-ml solution of diethylamine, triethanolamine, and cupric acetate in ethyl alcohol. The absorbance of the yellow-colored reaction product produced is read in a spectrophotometer and the concentration determined from a previously prepared calibration curve.

Sampling Procedure

The sampling rate through the fritted bubbler should be 0.5–1 lpm. A 30-minute sampling period should be adequate for the collection of carbon disulfide.

Interferences

No mention of interferences is made, and the method is thought to be specific for carbon disulfide. There is some indication in the literature that hydrogen sulfide and organic sulfur compounds containing a double-bonded sulfur atom will interfere.

The method is suitable for the determination of carbon disulfide in industrial hygiene work; with some modifications it could be used for stack gas analysis. Analysis requires less than 1 hour for completion.

This method is similar to that of Viles, but the reagent concentration is lower so that the blue color of the reagent does not interfere with the yellow color of the reaction. A filter can then be used in the photometer to remove all traces of the blue color.

Gunther, F. A., and R. C. Blinn. *Analysis of Insecticides and Acaricides* (New York: Interscience Publishers, Inc., 1955), p 338.

Carbon disulfide, in concentrations exceeding a few parts per million, can be determined rapidly and accurately by this method. The air sample is scrubbed through gas washing bottles or fritted glass bubblers, the first containing cupric sulfate and the second containing concentrated sulfuric acid. The first solution removes hydrogen sulfide and the second acts as a drying agent. The sample is then scrubbed through an absorption apparatus containing a mixture of diethylamine and cupric acetate solutions. It is then quantitatively transferred to a volumetric flask with methyl Cellosolve. This solution is allowed to stand for 20 minutes, after which the transmittance is read on a spectrophotometer at a wavelength of 380 mμ. Standards for the standard curve are prepared from pure carbon disulfide.

The sample is collected at a rate of about 50 ml for periods of time varying with the concentration expected. The collected sample should contain 5–50 μg carbon disulfide.

Interferences

The known interferences are hydrogen sulfide and those compounds containing double-bonded sulfur atoms. The interference by hydrogen sulfide is removed by the prescrubber containing cupric sulfate.

The determination is simple, rapid and requires no specialized equipment. It is suitable for industrial hygiene work but is not sensitive enough for most air pollution applications. Analysis can be completed in approximately 1 hour.

Hanson, N. W., D. A. Reilly, and H. E. Stagg, Eds. *The Determination of Toxic Substances in Air* (Cambridge, England: W. Heffer and Sons, Ltd., 1965), p 86.

See Also

Elkins, H. B. *The Chemistry of Industrial Toxicology*, 2nd ed. (New York: John Wiley and Sons, Inc., 1959), p 311.

Carbon disulfide, in concentrations ranging from 5–50 ppm in a 3-liter air sample, can be determined by this method. The air sample is collected in a fritted glass bubbler containing methyl alcohol, copper acetate in methyl alcohol, and diethylamine in benzene. After 15 minutes the yellow to brown color is visually compared with a set of standards and the concentration of carbon disulfide calculated.

The sampling rate through the fritted glass bubbler should be about).75 lpm until 3 liters of air have been sampled. Increasing or decreasing the sampling time will increase or decrease the sensitivity range of 5–50 ppm.

Interferences

The method is specific for carbon disulfide except in the presence of hydrogen sulfide. This interference can be removed by passing the air sample through lead acetate paper prior to bubbling through the sampling solution.

The method is simple and rapid, requiring approximately 20 minutes to complete the analysis. It is suitable for industrial hygiene work, and with a long sampling time (30–60 minutes) should be sensitive enough for air pollution work.

Jacobs, Morris B. *The Analytical Toxicology of Industrial Inorganic Poisons* (New York: Interscience Publishers, Inc., 1967), p 564.

To analyze for carbon disulfide in the presence of hydrogen sulfide collect the air sample in a series of five bubblers or gas washing bottles. The first three bubblers contain 100 ml of a cadmium chloride in dilute sodium hydroxide solution and are used to collect the hydrogen sulfide. The bubblers are charged with 100 ml of an alcoholic potassium hydroxide solution and will collect the carbon disulfide. The concentration of hydrogen disulfide can be determined iodometrically, and carbon disulfide can be determined by one of the methods abstracted elsewhere in this volume.

Jacobs, Morris B. *The Analytical Toxicology of Industrial Inorganic Poisons* (New York: Interscience Publishers, Inc., 1967), p 566.

To analyze for carbon disulfide vapors in the presence of methyl mercaptan and hydrogen sulfide, collect the air sample in two gas washing bottles containing a solution of sodium hydroxide followed by two fritted bubblers containing sodium hydroxide in ethanol. These bubblers are all connected in series. The contents of the gas washing bottles are combined and acidified with hydrochloric acid. Air is drawn through the sampling solution and led through two tubes, one containing calcium chloride, the other containing finely divided lead acetate. The second tube is connected to a small flask which contains a solution of isatin in sulfuric acid. Air is drawn through this entire system for approximately 30 minutes. Hydrogen sulfide can be determined from the color produced in the lead acetate, and the methyl mercaptan can be spectrophotometrically determined from the depth of the green color produced in the isatin–sulfuric acid solution.

The contents of the two fritted bubblers are combined and acidified with acetic acid, and a solution of cupric acetate is added. The solution is allowed to stand for two hours; then the yellow copper xanthate is filtered off. The concentration of carbon disulfide is determined from the quantity of copper present and the copper concentration is determined iodometrically.

Analysis requires 3–4 hours to complete. This method can be used in industrial hygiene work.

Carbon Monoxide

Berger, L. B., and H. H. Schrenk. **Methods for Detection and Determination of Carbon Monoxide,** U.S. Bur. Mines Techn. Paper **582** (1938).

Several methods for the determination of carbon monoxide are described. The discussion includes range of applicable concentrations, accuracy of the analysis, and the reactions occurring.

Grant, G. A., M. Katz, and R. L. Haines. **A Modified Iodine Pentoxide Method for the Determination of Carbon Monoxide,** Can. J. Technol. **29,** 43 (1951).

An improved iodine pentoxide method for the determination of carbon monoxide is described. This method of analysis provides a sensitivity of approximately 70 ppm.

Lysyj, I., J. E. Zarembo, and A. Hanley. **Rapid Method for Determination of Small Amounts of Carbon Monoxide in Gas Mixtures,** Anal. Chem. **31,** 902 (1959).

Carbon monoxide concentrations in excess of 1.5% can be determined with this method. The sample is collected in a 500-ml evacuated glass container having stopcocks at both ends. The sample is removed from the container by displacement with saturated sodium chloride solution. The sample is led through a combustion tube containing thermally decomposed silver permanganate and heated to 500°C to convert the carbon monoxide to carbon dioxide. The flow rate is maintained at around 20 ml per minute. The resulting carbon dioxide is taken up in a previously weighed Ascarite tube. The tube is again weighed after carbon dioxide absorption and the amount of carbon monoxide calculated from the weight difference.

Interferences

Provisions are made in the analytical procedure to protect against interference from carbon dioxide, water vapor, saturated hydrocarbons, and other atmospheric constituents.

Using a 500-ml sample, about 1.5% carbon monoxide can be determined quantitatively. If a larger sample is used, the lower limit can be extended somewhat.

The method is not sensitive enough for use in air pollution or industrial hygiene but can be used to determine the degree of catalyst poisoning and carbon monoxide in industrial processes, mine atmospheres, and exhaust gases.

Tebbett, R. W. **The Detection and Estimation of Carbon Monoxide,** Ann. Occupational Hyg. (London) **5,** 201 (1962).

Chemical and instrumental methods for the determination of carbon monoxide are detailed.

Levaggi, D. A., and M. Feldstein. **The Colorimetric Determination of Low Concentrations of Carbon Monoxide,** Am. Ind. Hyg. Assoc. J. **25,** 64 (1964).

Carbon monoxide, in concentrations from 5–1800 ppm, can be determined by this method. The air sample is collected in an evacuated flask. *p*-Sulfaminobenzoic acid, silver nitrate, and sodium hydroxide are mixed in a flask which is then evacuated. The air sample is introduced with a 50-ml syringe and the flask brought to atmospheric pressure with air free of CO. This flask is then mechanically shaken for 2 hours. The colloidal silver produced is read in a spectrophotometer at either 425 or 600 mμ. A calibration technique is also described for this analytical procedure.

Interferences

Acetylene and formaldehyde interfere with this determination. These materials can be removed by means of a special adsorbent consisting of mercuric oxide and sulfuric acid deposited on silica gel.

This method is applicable to industrial hygiene work as well as to the analysis of combustion products. Analysis requires 3–4 hours for completion.

Jacobs, Morris B. *The Analytical Toxicology of Industrial Inorganic Poisons* (New York: Interscience Publishers, Inc., 1967), p 713.

See Also

1. Sayers, R. R., and W. P. Yant. U.S. P.H.S. Reprint **872** (1924).
2. Sayers, R. R., W. P. Yant, and G. U. Jones. U.S.P.H.S. Reprint **872** (1924).

Carbon monoxide, in concentrations from 100–2000 ppm, can be accurately determined by this method. The sample is collected in a 250-ml flask by water displacement. A blood pipet is used to obtain a 0.1-cc sample of the normal blood, which is then diluted with water to 2 ml in the pipet. The diluted blood is quickly introduced into the flask containing the sample. The sample is then gently shaken for 20 minutes. Immediately after this period, the blood sample is quantitatively transferred to a test tube and a pyrogallic–tannic acid solution is added and thoroughly mixed. The sample is allowed to equilibrate with the blood for 30 minutes and compared with a set of prepared standards. The airborne concentration of carbon monoxide is then calculated.

Interferences

The method appears to be relatively specific for carbon monoxide. This method is not suitable for industrial hygiene work except in areas where the concentration is above the threshold limit value. The method is also not sensitive enough for air pollution work. It finds its greatest application in mine work. Complete analysis requires approximately 2.5 hours.

Jacobs, Morris B. *The Analytical Toxicology of Industrial Inorganic Poisons* (New York: Interscience Publishers, Inc., 1967), p 703.

See Also

Christman, A. A., W. D. Block, and J. Schultz. Ind. Eng. Chem., Anal. Ed. **9**, 153 (1937).

Carbon monoxide, in concentrations exceeding 500 ppm, can be determined by this method. The air sample is collected in an evacuated 500-ml flask. After collection of the sample, a palladium chloride and aluminum sulfate solution are added to the sample and allowed to stand for at least 4 hours. The resulting palladium metal is filtered. The filtrate is retained and potassium iodide and gum ghatti are added. The resulting red color produced is compared with a standard color in a colorimeter and the airborne concentration is calculated.

Interferences

Hydrogen sulfide and unsaturated hydrocarbons interfere with this determination. These interfering materials can be removed by scrubbing the air sample through bromine and potassium hydroxide.

The method is not sufficiently sensitive for industrial hygiene or air pollution work, but it is suitable for analysis of stack gases.

Jacobs, Morris B. *The Analytical Toxicology of Industrial Inorganic Poisons* (New York: Interscience Publishers, Inc., 1967), p 708.

See Also

Polis, R. D., L. B. Berger, and H. H. Schrenk. U.S. Bur. Mines, Rept. Invest. **3785** (1944).

Carbon monoxide, in concentrations above 10 ppm, can be determined by this method. The sample is collected by water displacement. Care must be taken during the entire procedure to insure that no extraneous air comes into contact with the sample. A solution of palladium chloride, phosphomolybdic acid and sulfuric acid are added rapidly to the sample. Acetone is then added quickly. The sample and a blank are then kept in a 60°C constant temperature bath for 1 hour. After cooling, the per cent transmission of the sample is read in a spectrophotometer at a wavelength of 650 mμ. The quantity of carbon monoxide present is read from a calibration curve, and the airborne concentration is calculated.

Interferences

This method appears to be relatively specific for carbon monoxide.

The method is suitable for industrial hygiene work. Analysis requires approximately 3 hours.

Carbon Tetrachloride

Jacobs, Morris B. *The Analytical Chemistry of Industrial Poisons, Hazards and Solvents*, 2nd ed. (New York: Interscience Publishers, Inc., 1949), p 577.

See Also

Cralley, L. V., T. E. Shea, and L. J. Cralley. J. Ind. Hyg. Toxicol. **25**, 172 (1943).

The air sample containing carbon tetrachloride is aspirated through two U-tubes, one containing magnesium perchlorate, the other containing silica gel. After collection, the sample is eluted from the silica gel with 95% ethyl alcohol. The sample is transferred to an Erlenmeyer flask and potassium hydroxide pellets are added. This mixture is heated overnight and then neutralized with acetic acid using phenolphthalein as an indicator. The chloride is determined titrimetrically with silver nitrate and potassium chromate. The airborne concentration of carbon tetrachloride is calculated.

Interferences

This method is not specific for carbon tetrachloride, and any halogenated compound will interfere.

Hanson, N. W., D. A. Reilly, and H. E. Stagg, Eds. *The Determination of Toxic Substances in Air* (Cambridge, England: W. Heffer and Sons, Ltd., 1965), p 97.

See Also

Rogers, G. W. and K. K. Kay.   J. Ind. Hyg. Toxicol. **29,** 229 (1947).

Carbon tetrachloride in concentrations from 8–80 ppm in a 1-liter air sample can be determined by this method. The air sample is collected in a midget impinger containing 10 ml of pyridine. The sample is quantitatively transferred to a flask and a measured amount of a standardized sodium hydroxide solution is added. The sample is heated in a water bath for 15 minutes and cooled. The optical density of the sample is read in a spectrophotometer at 525 mμ. The quantity of carbon tetrachloride is read from a calibration curve and the concentration of carbon tetrachloride in air is calculated.

The sampling rate through the impinger should be approximately 1 lpm. A 1-liter sample will provide a sensitivity range of 8–80 ppm. Increasing or decreasing the sampling duration will increase or decrease the sensitivity range obtainable.

Interferences

Chloroform, trichloroethylene and tetrachloroethylene will interfere with this determination. Hydrogen chloride at concentrations above 100 ppm and chlorine at concentrations above 50 ppm will also interfere.

This method is simple and rapid, requiring approximately 40 minutes to complete the analysis. This method requires no special or expensive apparatus and is applicable to industrial hygiene work. It is not considered sensitive enough for air pollution work.

Gunther, F. A., and R. C. Blinn.   *Analysis of Insecticides and Acaricides* (New York: Interscience Publishers, Inc., 1955), p 341.

See Also

Winteringham, F. P. W.   J. Soc. Chem. Ind. **61,** 186 (1942).

Carbon tetrachloride, in concentrations exceeding a few parts per million, can be determined by this method. The air sample is collected in a U-tube containing silica gel. After collection, the carbon tetrachloride is eluted from the silica with isopropyl alcohol. A portion of the sample and a few pellets of potassium hydroxide are placed in an oven at 50°C overnight. The sample is made just acid to phenolphthalein with acetic acid. The sample is then titrated with silver nitrate using potassium dichromate as the indicator. The concentration of carbon tetrachloride is calculated.

The sampling rate for the collection of carbon tetrachloride should be about 2 lpm for optimum efficiency. A sufficient sample must be collected to produce several milligrams of chloride for titration.

Interferences

The method is not specific for carbon tetrachloride because halide is actually determined. Any halogen-containing compound will interfere with the determination.

The determination is simple and rapid, requiring no specialized equipment to conduct the analysis. The method is suitable for industrial hygiene work as well as for analysis of pesticides in air.

Cellosolve Acetate

Goddu, R. F., N. F. Le Blanc, and C. M. Wright. **Spectrophotometric Determination of Esters and Anhydrides by Hydroxamic Acid Reaction,** Anal. Chem. **27,** 1251 (1955).

See Also

Hill, V. T. Ind. Eng. Chem., Anal. Ed. **18,** 317 (1946).

Cellosolve acetate, in concentrations above 20 ppm in a 25-liter air sample, can be determined by this method. The sample is collected in two fritted bubblers connected in series, each containing ethyl alcohol. The sample is reacted with an alkaline hydroxylamine solution. The addition of ferric ion to this mixture produces a highly colored product. The absorbance of this product is read at a wavelength of 530 mμ. The quantity of ester present is read from a calibration curve and the airborne concentration is calculated.

Sampling Procedure

The air sample may be collected in two fritted bubblers connected in series, each containing 10 ml ethyl alcohol. The sampling rate should be approximately 1–2 lpm until at least 25 liters of air have been sampled.

Interferences

Any other ester, anhydrides, aldehydes, and isocyanates will interfere with this determination.

Analysis requires approximately 2 hours. This method is applicable to industrial hygiene work but is not sufficiently sensitive for air pollution work.

Chloretone

Jacobs, M. B. *The Analytical Chemistry of Industrial Poisons, Hazards and Solvents,* 2nd ed. (New York: Interscience Publishers, Inc., 1949), p 565.

See Also

1. Cole, W. H.   J. Biol. Chem. **71,** 173 (1926).
2. Gettler, A. O., and H. Blume.   Arch. Pathol. **11,** 555 (1931).
3. Ross, J. H.   J. Biol. Chem. **58,** 641 (1923/24).

Chloretone in the parts per million range can be determine↳ ↳y this method. The air sample is collected in a bubbler containing 95% ethyl alcohol. After collection, the sample is quantitatively transferred to a volumetric flask and diluted to volume. Pyridine, sodium ˙ vdroxide, and an aliquot of the sample are placed in a test tube and h↳ ˙ted in a water bath for 1 minute. The resulting color in the pyridine layer is compared with a set of color standards in a color comparator. The permanent color standards are prepared from basic fuchsin in acidified ethyl alcohol. The concentration of chloretone in air is calculated.

Sampling Procedure

The air sample is collected in a bubbler containing either dilute hydrochloric acid or ethyl alcohol. A sampling rate of 2 lpm for at least 30 minutes should provide an adequate sample.

Interferences

Any material with a 3 halogen-carbon linkage will interfere with this determination. Examples of such compounds are bromoform, iodoform, Chloretone and chloral.

Analysis requires approximately 1 hour. This method is applicable to industrial hygiene work but is not sufficiently sensitive for air pollution analysis.

Chlorinated Hydrocarbons

Hanson, N. W., D. A. Reilly, and H. E. Stagg, Eds. *The Determination of Toxic Substances in Air* (Cambridge, England: W. Heffer and Sons, Ltd., 1965), p 91.

Organic chlorinated hydrocarbons, in concentrations from 50–350 μg chlorine, can be determined by this method. The air sample is collected in a midget impinger containing 20 ml ethanolamine. The sample is quantitatively transferred to a refluxing apparatus, dioxane is added, and the solution is refluxed three times with 0.3 g sodium each time. Refluxing is continued for 30 minutes after the last sodium addition. The sample is then acidified with 50:50 nitric acid. The solution is filtered to remove any particles that might be present and transferred to a Nessler tube. Silver nitrate is added, and the solution is diluted to 100 ml. It is then allowed to stand in the dark for 5 minutes. The turbidity of the sample is compared with that of a set of standards. The concentration of the organic chlorinated hydrocarbon is then calculated knowing the concentration of chloride, the chlorinated hydrocarbon present, and the volume of air sampled.

The sampling rate should be about 175 ml per minute for a period long enough to collect 50–350 μg of chloride.

Interferences

This is a nonspecific method and is applicable to any chlorinated organic compound.

The method is simple and relatively rapid, requiring approximately 1.5 hours for complete analysis. It requires no special or expensive equipment and is applicable to industrial hygiene work, but it is considered not sufficiently sensitive for air pollution work.

Chlorine

Porter, L. E. **Free Chlorine in Air, a Colorimetric Method for Its Estimation**, Ind. Eng. Chem. 18, 731 (1926).

A method for the determination of chlorine in air is described. A simple sampling arrangement requiring no power is used to collect the sample. The sampling solution is *o*-tolidine, which exhibits a yellow color after contact with chlorine. The color is compared with a series of standards in Nessler tubes and the airborne concentration is calculated.

This method requires approximately 30 minutes for complete analysis and can be used as a field method in industrial hygiene.

Hanson, N. W., D. A. Reilly, and H. E. Stagg, Eds. *The Determination of Toxic Substances in Air* (Cambridge, England: W. Heffer and Sons, Ltd., 1965), p 43.

Chlorine, in concentrations from 1–5 ppm in a 3-liter air sample, can be determined by this method. The air sample is collected in a midget impinger containing 10 ml of a solution of *o*-tolidine in hydrochloric acid. Sampling continues until the color in the sample is equivalent to one of the standards previously prepared from potassium dichromate. The airborne concentration of chlorine is calculated from the volume of air sampled and the weight of chlorine in the sample, which is determined from the known standard.

The sampling rate through the impinger containing the *o*-tolidine reagent should be about 0.75 lpm and the duration depends on the time required to produce the yellow color in the sampling solution.

Interferences

The method is relatively specific for chlorine although other materials easily releasing chlorine from their molecules will produce an interference.

The method is simple and rapid, requiring about 30 minutes for complete analysis. No special or expensive equipment is required. This method is suitable for industrial hygiene work and air pollution work, but the latter requires a relatively long sampling time because of the small amounts of chlorine occurring in the atmosphere.

Jacobs, Morris B. *The Analytical Toxicology of Industrial Inorganic Poisons* (New York: Interscience Publishers, Inc., 1967), p 636.

Chlorine, in concentrations above 0.3 ppm in a 5-liter air sample, can be determined by this method. The air sample is collected in a fritted bubbler or gas washing bottle containing distilled water. A 100-ml sample or an aliquot diluted to 100 ml is transferred to a Nessler tube. *o*-Tolidine reagent is added and the color developed in the dark for 5–15 minutes. The resulting yellow color is compared with a series of color standards prepared from potassium dichromate and copper sulfate. The airborne concentration of chlorine is then calculated.

Sampling Procedure

The air sample may be collected at a rate of 1 lpm for 5 minutes if collected in a bubbler or gas washing bottle containing 100 ml of distilled water.

Interferences

Iron, manganese, and nitrite interfere with this analysis; bromine and other halogens may also interfere.

This method requires approximately 1 hour for complete analysis. It is suitable for industrial hygiene and air pollution work, but a long sampling duration may be required in the latter case.

Jacobs, Morris B. *The Analytical Toxicology of Industrial Inorganic Poisons* (New York: Interscience Publishers, Inc., 1967), p 639.

See Also

Dept. Sci. Ind. Research Brit. Leaflet **10** (1939).

This is a field method for the determination of chlorine. The air sample is collected in a special bubbler containing a solution of *o*-tolidine. After collection the color of the sample is compared with a set of sealed standards and the airborne concentration of chlorine is calculated.

Interferences

Iron, manganese, nitrite F, bromine and other halogens may interfere with this analysis.

Chlorine Dioxide

Jacobs, Morris B. *The Analytical Chemistry of Industrial Poisons, Hazards, and Solvents,* 2nd ed. (New York: Interscience Publishers, Inc., 1949), p 382.

Chlorine dioxide, in the parts per million range, can be determined by this method. The air sample is collected in a midget impinger containing 10 ml of a potassium iodide solution. A sampling rate of approximately 1 lpm for 30 minutes should provide a sufficient sample for most analytical applications. The sample is quantitatively transferred to an Erlenmeyer flask and the chlorine dioxide determined iodometrically.

Interferences

The method is not specific for chlorine dioxide, and any substance liberating iodine from potassium iodide will interfere with this analysis.

This method requires approximately 1 hour for complete analysis. It is suitable for industrial hygiene but is not sufficiently sensitive or specific for air pollution analysis.

Jacobs, Morris B. *The Analytical Toxicology Of Industrial Inorganic Poisons* (New York: Interscience Publishers, Inc., 1967), p 645.

Chlorine dioxide in air is collected in a bubbler containing a potassium iodide solution. The sample is titrated with a standardized sodium thiosulfate solution.

Sampling Procedure

The sample is collected in a fritted bubbler containing 10 ml of a potassium iodide solution at a rate of 1 lpm for 30 minutes.

o-Chloroaniline

Hanson, N. W., D. A. Reilly, and H. E. Stagg, Eds. *The Determination of Toxic Substances in Air* (Cambridge, England: W. Heffer and Sons, Ltd., 1965), p 56.

o-Chloroaniline, in concentrations above 1 μg per 10 of hydrochloric acid sampling solution, can be determined quickly and easily by this method. The sample is collected in a fritted bubbler containing 10 ml of a standardized hydrochloric acid solution. It is quantitatively transferred to a volumetric flask. A sodium nitrite solution is added and allowed to stand for 15 minutes at a temperature below 15°C. Sodium sulfamate, sodium acetate, *N*-sulfatoethyl-*m*-toluidine and hydrochloric acid are added. Full color development occurs in 1 hour. The optical density of the solution is read on a spectrophotometer at a wavelength of 500 mμ. The quantity of *o*-chloroaniline present is determined from a previously prepared calibration curve and the airborne concentration is calculated.

The sampling rate through the fritted bubbler should be approximately 5 lpm. The duration of sampling depends on the expected concentration of the amine.

Interferences

Many amines and their derivatives interfere with this method. The method is relatively simple and requires about 2 hours to complete the analysis. No special or expensive equipment is required, and the method is suitable for industrial hygiene work.

Chlorobenzene

Jacobs, Morris B. *The Analytical Chemistry of Industrial Poisons, Hazards and Solvents,* 2nd ed. (New York: Interscience Publishers, Inc., 1949), p 594.

See Also

1. Schrenk, H. H., S. J. Pearce, and W. P. Yant. U.S. Bur. Mines, Rept. Invest. **3287** (1935).
2. Pearce, S. J., H. H. Schrenk, and W. P. Yant. U.S. Bur. Mines, Rept. Invest. **3302** (1936).

Chlorobenzene, in concentrations above 25 ppm, can be determined by this method if a 0.5-liter air sample is collected. This limit can be extended by increasing the sampling time significantly. The air sample is collected by sampling through a special bubbler which contains a nitrating acid composed of equal quantities of concentrated sulfuric acid and fuming nitric acid. After collection, the sample is allowed to react for 30 minutes to insure complete nitration. The sample is quantitatively transferred to an Erlenmeyer flask and cooled below 20°C. It is neutralized by adding sodium hydroxide slowly and carefully. The solution is warmed to 30°C, and 10 ml of methyl ethyl ketone (butanone) are added. It is then transferred to a separatory funnel and the water drawn off. Sodium hydroxide is added and the color is allowed to develop for 1 hour. The resulting red color is compared with a set of standards and the quantity present in the sample is determined. The airborne concentration is calculated.

Sampling Procedure

The sample is collected in a special bubbler containing nitrating acid. A sampling rate of 30 ml per minute for approximately 1 hour should provide a sufficient sample for analysis.

Interferences

Toluene, benzene, ethylbenzene, styrene, and xylene will interfere with this determination.

The method requires approximately 3 hours for complete analysis. If a 60-minute sample is collected, the method is suitable for industrial hygiene work but is not sufficiently sensitive for air pollution work.

Hanson, N. W., D. A. Reilly, and H. E. Stagg, Eds. *The Determination of Toxic Substances in Air* (Cambridge, England: W. Heffer and Sons, Ltd., 1965), p 107.

See Also

Gage, J. C.   Analyst **84**, 509 (1959).

Chlorobenzene, in concentrations from 20–200 ppm in an air sample of 0.5 liters, can be determined by this method. The air sample is collected in a fritted glass bubbler containing 10 ml of a paraformaldehyde–sulfuric acid solution. Thirty minutes after collecting the sample, its optical density is read in a spectrophotometer at a wavelength of 485 mμ. The quantity of chlorobenzene is read from a previously prepared calibration curve, and the airborne concentration is calculated.

The sampling rate through the fritted bubbler containing paraformaldehyde–sulfuric acid mixture should be about 200 ml per minute. If a 500-ml sample is collected, a sensitivity range of 20–200 ppm can be expected. Increasing or decreasing the volume of air sample will increase or decrease the concentration that can be determined by this method.

Interferences

This method is not specific for chlorobenzene, and most of the aromatic hydrocarbons will produce some type of color with this reagent.

The method is simple and rapid, requiring less than 1 hour for complete analysis. No special or expensive equipment is required and the method is suitable for industrial hygiene work. It is not considered sufficiently sensitive for air pollution work.

Chloroform

Jacobs, M. B.   *The Analytical Chemistry of Industrial Poisons, Hazards and Solvents*, 2nd ed. (New York: Interscience Publishers, Inc., 1949), p 565.

See Also

1. Cole, W. H.   J. Biol. Chem. **71**, 173 (1926).
2. Gettler, A. O., and H. Blume.   Arch. Pathol. **11**, 555 (1931).
3. Ross, J. H.   J. Biol. Chem. **58**, 641 (1923/24).

Chloroform in the parts per million range can be determined by this method. The air sample is collected in a bubbler containing 95% ethyl alcohol. After collection, the sample is quantitatively transferred to a volumetric flask and diluted to volume. Pyridine, sodium hydroxide, and an aliquot of the sample are placed in a test tube and heated in a water bath for 1 minute. The resulting color in the pyridine layer is compared with a set of color standards in a color comparator. The permanent color standards are prepared from basic fuchsin in acidified ethyl alcohol. The concentration of chloroform in air is calculated.

Sampling Procedure

The air sample is collected in a bubbler containing either dilute hydrochloric acid or ethyl alcohol. A sampling rate of 2 lpm for at least 30 minutes should provide an adequate sample.

Interferences

Any material with a 3 halogen-carbon linkage will interfere with this determination. Examples of such compounds are bromoform, iodoform, Chloretone and chloral.

Analysis requires approximately 1 hour. The method is applicable to industrial hygiene work but is not sufficiently sensitive for air pollution analysis.

Hanson, N. W., D. A. Reilly, and H. E. Stagg, Eds. *The Determination of Toxic Substances in Air* (Cambridge: England: W. Heffer and Sons, Ltd., 1965), p 99.

See Also

1. Brumbaugh, J. H., and D. E. Stallard. J. Agr. Food Chem. **6**, 465 (1958).
2. Rogers, G. W., and K. K. Kay. J. Ind. Hyg. Toxicol. **29**, 8229 (1947).

Chloroform, in concentrations from 10–200 μg in 10 ml of sampling solution, can be determined by this method. The air sample is collected in a midget impinger containing 10 ml pyridine. After sampling, an accurately measured volume of a standardized sodium hydroxide solution is added to the sample which is then heated for 5 minutes in a water bath and cooled. The optical density of the solution is then read in a spectrophotometer at 525 mμ. The quantity of chloroform is read from a previously prepared calibration curve, and the airborne concentration of chloroform is calculated.

A sampling rate of 0.5 lpm should be adequate, and a 0.5-liter sample should provide a sensitivity range of 10–200 μg in 10 ml of sampling solution. Concentrations higher or lower than the specified range may be obtained by increasing or decreasing the sample size.

Interferences

Trichloroethylene and tetrachloroethane interfere with this determination.

The method is simple and rapid, requiring approximately 30 minutes to complete the analysis. This method requires no special or expensive equipment and is suitable for industrial hygiene work. It is not considered sufficiently sensitive for air pollution work.

1-Chloro-1-Nitrobutane

Jones, L. R., and J. A. Reddick.   **Colorimetric Determination of Nitroparaffins,** Anal. Chem. **24,** 1533 (1952).

1-Chloro-1-nitrobutane in concentrations above 3 μg in the sample analyzed can be determined by this method. The sample is collected in two fritted bubblers containing concentrated sulfuric acid. An aliquot of the sample, up to 10 ml, is quantitatively transferred to a test tube, held in a boiling water bath for 5 minutes, and cooled. Resorcinol solution is then placed on top of the acid and the sample slowly mixed. The sample is heated in a water bath and cooled. The optical density of the resulting red-blue color is read in a spectrophotometer at a wavelength of 560 $m\mu$. The quantity of 1-chloro-1-nitrobutane present is read from a calibration curve and the airborne concentration is calculated.

Sampling Procedure

The sample is collected in two bubblers, series connected, containing sulfuric acid. A sampling rate of 2 lpm for a period long enough to collect 5–10 μg will provide an adequate sample.

Interferences

Any aliphatic nitroparaffin will interfere with this determination. Complete analysis requires approximately 30 minutes. The method is suitable for industrial hygiene work, and, if a sufficiently large sample is collected, it is also applicable to air pollution work.

1-Chloro-1-Nitropropane

Jacobs, Morris B. *The Analytical Chemistry of Industrial Poisons, Hazards and Solvents,* 2nd ed. (New York: Interscience Publishers, Inc., 1949), p 738.

1-Chloro-1-nitropropane, in the parts per million range, can be determined by this method. The sample is collected in a fritted bubbler containing absolute ethyl alcohol. A 1-ml aliquot containing less than 600 μg of 1-chloro-1-nitropropane is used for analysis. Phenylhydrazine in alcohol and sulfuric acid is added to the sample which is then cooled. Concentrated sulfuric acid is added and the sample is heated in a water bath for 1 hour at 100°C. The sample is diluted with sulfuric acid and the absorption of the resulting red color is read in a spectrophotometer at a wavelength of 540 mμ. The quantity of 1-chloro-1-nitropropane present in the sample is determined from a calibration curve, and the airborne concentration is calculated.

Sampling Procedure

The sample may be collected in a fritted bubbler containing 10 ml absolute ethyl alcohol. To prevent rapid evaporation, the impinger can be immersed in an ice bath. A sampling rate of 1 lpm for 30 minutes usually provides a sufficient sample.

Interferences

Other chloronitroparaffins may interfere with this method.

The method requires approximately 2 hours for complete analysis. It is suitable for industrial hygiene work but is not sufficiently sensitive for air pollution work.

Chloropicrin

Gunther, F. A., and R. C. Blinn. *Analysis of Insecticides and Acaricides* (New York: Interscience Publishers, Inc., 1955), p 39.

See Also

Feinsilver, L., and F. W. Oberst. Anal. Chem. **25,** 820 (1953).

Chloropicrin, in concentrations exceeding a few parts per million, can be determined quickly and accurately by this method. The sample is collected in a fritted bubbler or gas washing bottle containing iso-propyl alcohol. After collection of the sample, sodium peroxide is added and the mixture is refluxed for approximately 30 minutes. After cooling, the sample is transferred quantitatively to a volumetric flask and phe-nolphthalein is added. It is treated with hydrochloric acid until the pink coloration from the indicator disappears. Sulfanilic acid is added and the mixture allowed to stand for 1 minute, at which time 1-naph-thylethylenediamine dihydrochloride is added. After 15 minutes the transmittance of the solution is read in a spectrophotometer at 540 mμ. The standard curve is constructed using pure chloropicrin treated ex-actly as the samples.

The sampling rate for the collection of chloropicrin should be 0.5–1 lpm through a 125-ml gas washing bottle.

Interferences

This method is not specific for chloropicrin since any aliphatic sec-ondary nitro compound will cause interference. Some of the aromatic nitro compounds will also interfere.

The determination is simple and rapid, requiring no special or ex-pensive equipment. About 3 hours are required for completion of anal-ysis. The method is suitable for industrial hygiene work and pesticide analysis but is not sufficiently sensitive for air pollution work.

o-Cresol

Jacobs, Morris B. *The Analytical Chemistry of Industrial Poisons, Hazards and Solvents,* 2nd ed. (New York: Interscience Publishers, Inc., 1949), p 698.

See Also

Scott, R. D.   Ind. Eng. Chem., Anal. Ed. 3, 67 (1931).

Cresol in quantities greater than 10 mg can be determined by this method. The sample is collected in a fritted bubbler or gas washing bottle containing a normal sodium hydroxide solution. After collection, the sample is quantitatively transferred to an Erlenmeyer flask, neu-tralized and diluted to 200 ml with distilled water. Potassium bromide solution and hydrochloric acid solution are added to the sample, which is then placed in a water bath at 25°C for 1 hour. Potassium bromate is added and the solution is maintained at 25° ± 1°C for 1 hour. Potas-sium iodide is added and after 0.5 hours the liberated iodine in the sample is titrated with a standard sodium thiosulfate solution. The airborne concentration of cresol is then calculated.

Sampling Procedure

The sample may be collected in a gas washing bottle containing 50 ml of sodium hydroxide solution at the rate of 0.5 cfm for a period depending upon the expected concentration of cresol.

Interferences

This method will not determine a specific cresol but will determine all cresols. The presence of cresols or aromatic amines will also interfere with the analysis.

The method is suitable for industrial hygiene work but is not sufficiently sensitive for air pollution work.

Carney, G. E., and W. K. Sanford. **Ultraviolet Analysis of Isomeric Cresol Mixtures**, Anal. Chem. **25**, 1417 (1953).
See Also
Houghton, J. A., and G. Lee. Am. Ind. Hyg. Assoc. J. **21**, 219 (1960).

o-Cresol, in concentrations from 0.3–4.5 ppm, can be determined by this method if a 25-liter air sample is collected. The air sample is collected in a gas washing bottle containing highly purified ethanol at a rate of 3 lpm. After collection, the sample absorbance is read in a spectrophotometer at a wavelength of 272 mμ. The concentration of *o*-cresol present is read from a calibration curve and the airborne concentration is calculated.

Interferences

Any material absorbing at a wavelength of 272 mμ will interfere.

The method is suitable for industrial hygiene work and requires less than 1 hour for complete analysis.

Chromyl Chloride

Hill, W. H., and F. X. Worden. **Chromyl Chloride—A Possibly Important Industrial Air Contaminant**, Am. Ind. Hyg. Assoc. J. **23**, 186 (1962).

Chromyl chloride, in concentrations from less than two to twenty μg per ml, can be determined by this method. The air sample is first passed through a glass fiber filter to remove any chromium-containing dusts. The sample is led through a scrubber containing concentrated sulfuric acid to remove moisture, and finally the chromyl chloride is absorbed in a bubbler containing carbon tetrachloride. The resulting solution is then read in a spectrophotometer at 425 mμ and the concentration of chromyl chloride determined from a previously prepared calibration curve.

The sampling rate can vary from 1–2 lpm to 1 cfm depending on the concentration of chromyl chloride expected and the size of the bubbler used.

Interferences

If the sample is collected as described above, interferences should be negligible. The method is quantitative and simple to use. Analysis requires less than 1 hour including construction of a calibration curve. The method is applicable to industrial hygiene work but is probably not sensitive enough for air pollution work.

Crotonaldehyde

Altshuller, A. P., and I. R. Cohen. **Spectrophotometric Determination of Crotonaldehyde with 4-Hexylresorcinol,** Anal. Chem. 33, 1180 (1961).

Crotonaldehyde, in the concentration range of 1–20 μg per ml of sampling solution, can be determined by this method. No sampling procedure is discussed but it seems that an air sample could be collected in ethyl alcohol contained in a midget or Greenburg-Smith impinger.

Alcoholic 4-hexylresorcinol–alcoholic mercuric chloride solution, and saturated trichloroacetic acid are added to a portion of the alcoholic sample. The reactants are then heated to 60°C for 20 minutes and cooled to room temperature. The absorbance of the solution is read at 385 mμ and the quantity of crotonaldehyde present is read from a calibration curve.

Sampling rates were not discussed, but if a midget impinger is used a rate of 0.1 cfm would appear to be adequate. If the Greenburg-Smith impinger is used, a sampling rate of 1 cfm would appear to be reasonable.

Interferences

Saturated aldehydes, ketones, alcohols, esters, acids, most hydrocarbons, and phenols do not interfere significantly. Unsaturated aldehydes and ketones as well as diolefins and nitrogen dioxide do interfere.

Complete analysis requires approximately 1 hour. This method is suitable for industrial hygiene work and can be used for air pollution work if a sufficiently large air sample is collected.

Sawicki, E., T. R. Hauser, T. W. Stanley, and W. Elbert. **The 3-Methyl-2-Benzothiazolone Hydrozone Test. Sensitive New Methods for the Detection, Rapid Estimation and Determination of Aliphatic Aldehydes,** Anal. Chem. 33, 93 (1961).

Crotonaldehyde can be analyzed in quantities as low as 5 μg per 100 ml of solution. Crotonaldehyde and other aliphatic aldehydes can be determined specifically if only one of these compounds is present in the contaminated air.

Air is sampled through an impinger containing a collecting solution of 10 ml of 3-methyl-2-benzothiazolone and distilled water. The solution is transferred to a volumetric flask and aqueous ferric chloride is added. The mixture is then diluted to 100 ml with acetone. Th absorbance of the resulting blue color is read in a spectrophotometer at 670 mμ and the quantity of aldehyde present is read from a calibration curve.

Sampling Procedure

A sampling rate of 2 lpm through a midget impinger containing 10 ml of solution should be satisfactory for collection of the aldehyde.

Interferences

Other aliphatic aldehydes interfere, and if they exist singly in the air to be sampled they can be accurately determined by this method. Also thought to interfere are aniline, N-alkylanilines, N,N-dialkylanilines, indoles, carbozoles, and phenothiazines.

The method is quantitative for crotonaldehyde from a concentration of 5–125 μ per 100 ml of solution. The method is applicable to air and auto exhaust analysis and requires approximately 30 minutes to complete.

Kwan, T. W., and B. M. Watts. **A New Color Reaction of Anthrone with Malonaldehyde and Other Aliphatic Aldehydes,** Anal. Chem. **35,** 733 (1963).

A method is described for the analysis of crotonaldehyde using anthrone as the color-forming reagent. This method appears to be applicable to air samples containing elevated concentrations of the aldehyde. More work needs to be done to determine sampling solution, sampling rates and sensitivities before the method can be used routinely.

Alcorn, R. A. **Fluorometric Determination of Acrolein and Related Compounds with *m*-Aminophenol,** Anal. Chem. **40,** 1704 (1968).

Crotonaldehyde, in concentrations above 0.02 μg per ml, can be determined by this method. A 2-ml aliquot of the sample is quantitatively transferred to a test tube with *m*-aminophenol and hydroxylamine hydrochloride in hydrochloric acid. If the sample is collected in water, it is heated for 10 minutes in boiling water; if collected in ethyl alcohol, it is heated for 45 minutes at 65°C. After cooling, the sample fluorescence is read at a wavelength of 495 mμ. The quantity of crotonaldehyde present is read from a calibration curve and the airborne concentration is calculated.

Sampling Procedure

This method was not designed specifically for air analysis but should be applicable particularly to air pollution work because of the sensitivity of the technique. It appears to be possible to collect the sample in ethyl alcohol or water in a midget impinger for a period exceeding 10 minutes. If the sample is collected in water, two impingers in series should be used. If the sample is collected in ethyl alcohol the impinger should be immersed in an ice bath to minimize the evaporative losses.

Interferences

Other aldehydes and compounds producing crotonaldehyde after hydrolysis interfere with this determination.

The method requires approximately 2 hours for complete analysis and should be applicable to both industrial hygiene and air pollution work.

Cyanogen

Jacobs, Morris B. *The Analytical Toxicology of Industrial Inorganic Poisons* (New York: Interscience Publishers, Inc., 1967), p 732.
See Also
Francis, C. K., and W. B. Connell. J. Am. Chem. Soc. **35**, 1624 (1913).

Cyanogen, in concentrations above approximately 3 μg per volume of sample analyzed, can be determined by this method. The air sample is collected in two fritted bubblers connected in series, each containing 15 cc of a dilute sodium hydroxide solution. The sample is quantitatively transferred to a suitable volumetric flask (25 cc) and brought to volume. A portion, or all, of the sample is placed in an evaporating dish along with a small volume of ammonium polysulfide solution, stirred and evaporated to dryness. The residue is taken up in a little water; a cadmium nitrate solution is added and the solutions are filtered and placed in a Nessler tube. Sulfuric acid and ferric chloride are added to the sample, and the resulting red color is compared with a series of standards prepared from potassium cyanide. The airborne concentration of hydrogen cyanide is calculated.

Sampling Procedure

The sample is collected in two bubblers in series each containing 15 ml of a dilute sodium hydroxide solution. The sample is collected at a rate of 0.5 lpm for 30 minutes or longer if the expected concentration is small.

Interferences

Any other cyanide or cyanate will interfere with this determination.
The method is suitable for industrial hygiene work, and, if a sufficiently long sampling duration is used, the method can be applied to air pollution analysis. Analysis requires approximately 1.5 hours.

Jacobs, Morris B. *The Analytical Toxicology of Industrial Inorganic Poisons* (New York: Interscience Publishers, Inc., 1967), p 730.

Cyanogen, in concentrations of 20 μg per ml of sample, can be determined by this method. The air sample is collected in two fritted bubblers connected in series, each containing 10 ml of potassium hydroxide to which a few drops of ferrous sulfate solution have been added. After collection, the sample is quantitatively transferred to a beaker and brought to a boil to facilitate the production of ferrocyanide. The sample is cooled, filtered and acidified. A small quantity of ferric chloride is added. The blue color produced is compared with a set of standard solutions prepared from potassium cyanide.

Sampling Procedure

The sample is collected in two bubblers in series at a rate of 2 lpm. Depending upon the expected concentration, up to 100 liters of air may be collected.

Interferences

The method is relatively specific for hydrogen cyanide. Cyanogen and probably cyanogen chloride interfere as does any material producing cyanide ion.

The sensitivity of the method leaves something to be desired but it can be used in industrial hygiene work. It is not sufficiently sensitive for air pollution work. The method requires approximately 1 hour for complete analysis.

Cyanogen Bromide

Jacobs, Morris B. *The Analytical Toxicology of Industrial Inorganic Poisons* (New York: Interscience Publishers, Inc., 1967), p 730.

Cyanogen bromide, in concentrations of 20 μg per ml of sample, can be determined by this method. The air sample is collected in two fritted bubblers connected in series, each containing 10 ml of potassium hydroxide to which a few drops of ferrous sulfate solution have been added. After collection, the sample is quantitatively transferred to a beaker and brought to a boil to facilitate the production of ferrocyanide. The sample is cooled, filtered and acidified. A small quantity of ferric chloride is added. The blue color produced is compared with a set of standard solutions prepared from potassium cyanide.

Sampling Procedure

The sample is collected in two bubblers in series at a rate of 2 lpm. Depending upon the expected concentration, up to 100 liters of air may be collected.

Interferences

The method is relatively specific for hydrogen cyanide. Cyanogen and probably cyanogen chloride interfere as does any material producing cyanide ion.

The sensitivity of the method leaves something to be desired but it can be used in industrial hygiene work. It is not sufficiently sensitive for air pollution work. The method requires approximately 1 hour for complete analysis.

Cyanogen Chloride

Jacobs, Morris B. *The Analytical Toxicology of Industrial Inorganic Poisons* (New York: Interscience Publishers, Inc., 1967), p 729.

See Also
1. Nicholson, R. I.   Analyst **66**, 189 (1941).
2. Epstein, J.   Anal. Chem. **19**, 272 (1947).

Cyanogen chloride, in concentrations from 0.2–1.2 μg per ml, can be determined by this method. The sample is collected in a fritted bubbler containing water as the collecting medium. One ml of the sample is quantitatively transferred to a test tube. After 1 minute a solution of 3-methyl-1-phenyl-5-pyrazolone in pyridine is added to the sample. After 20 minutes the optical density of the resulting solution is read in a spectrophotometer at a wavelength of 630 mμ. The quantity of cyanide present in the aliquot analyzed is read from a calibration curve prepared from sodium cyanide, and the airborne concentration is calculated.

Sampling Procedure

The sample is collected in a fritted bubbler at a rate of 2–3 lpm for 30 minutes.

Interferences

The method appears to be relatively specific for cyanide ion including hydrogen cyanide. This method is suitable for industrial hygiene work. In order to collect a sample containing enough cyanide for the method to be considered useful for air pollution work, however, a very long sampling time is required.

The preparation of the pyrazolone reagent requires approximately 5 hours while the rest of the analysis can be completed in 1 hour.

Decaborane

Pfitzer, E. A., and J. M. Seals. **Determination of Decaborane with Dipyridyl Ethylene,** Am. Ind. Hyg. Assoc. J. **20,** 392 (1959).

Decaborane, in concentrations exceeding 0.01 ppm, can be determined by this method. The air sample is collected in a reagent consisting of 1,2-bis(4-pyridyl)-ethylene in xylene. When air containing decaborane is scrubbed through this reagent, a clear pink-to-red color is formed. The optical density of this colored solution is read on a spectrophotometer at 515 mμ. The concentration is read from a calibration curve.

The method is applicable to industrial hygiene work and requires about 1 hour for completion.

Dibenzylamine

Hong, W. H., and K. A. Conners. **Spectrophotometric Determination of Aliphatic Amines by Acylation with Cinnamic Anhydride,** Anal. Chem. **40,** 1273 (1968).

Dibenzylamine, in concentrations at the parts per million level, can be determined by this method. This method was not designed specifically for air analysis but appears to be applicable. A 1-ml aliquot of the sample is quantitatively transferred to a 50-ml volumetric flask. Cinnamic anhydride solution and tri-*n*-butylamine in acetonitrile are added, mixed, and allowed to react at room temperature for several minutes. Sodium hydroxide is added to the 50-ml mark and allowed to stand for 10 minutes. The sample mixture is quantitatively transferred to a separatory funnel and extracted with chloroform. The chloroform extract is washed with distilled water and filtered into a 50-ml volumetric flask. The sample is made to volume with chloroform, and the absorbance of the sample is read in a spectrophotometer at 283 mμ. The airborne concentration of dibenzylamine is calculated.

Sampling Procedure

An air sampling procedure must be developed. Collection might be accomplished using a fritted bubbler containing an acetonitrile solution.

Interferences

Any aliphatic amine will interfere with this method.

Diborane

Long, J. E., G. J. Levinskas, W. H. Hill, and J. L. Svirbely. **Gas-Mask Protection Against Diborane, Pentaborane, and Mixtures of Boranes,** A.M.A. Arch. Ind. Health **16,** 393 (1957).

See Also

1. Feinsilver, L. *Quantitative Determination of Diborane in Air,* Chemical Corps Medical Laboratories, Research Report No. 170, 1953.
2. Hatcher, J. T., and L. V. Wilcox. Anal. Chem. **22,** 567 (1950).
3. Kolthoff, I. M., and E. B. Sandell. *Textbook of Quantitative Inorganic Analysis,* rev. ed. (New York: Macmillan Co., 1943), p 560.

Diborane, in concentrations above 1 μg per total sample, can be analyzed by this method. The sample is collected in three gas washing bottles containing 30 ml distilled water slightly acidified by the addition of one drop concentrated hydrochloric acid. The samples are maintained at 58°C during collection to promote hydrolysis of diborane. The sampling rate should be 1 lpm. After collection, the sample can be analyzed by the carmine method, as described in Reference 2 above.

Interferences

Boric acid and borates interfere. Pentaborane and decaborane interfere only slightly.

The method requires approximately 2 hours for complete analysis. It is suitable for industrial hygiene and air pollution work.

Dichloroethyl Ether

Jacobs, Morris B. *The Analytical Chemistry of Industrial Poisons, Hazards, and Solvents,* 2nd ed. (New York: Interscience Publishers, Inc., 1949), p 609.

Dichloroethyl ether, in the parts per million range, can be determined by this method. The sample is collected in fritted bubblers containing a saturated solution of alkaline potassium hydroxide. The sample is refluxed to hydrolyze the sample and liberate the chloride. The chloride is then determined by an applicable method.

Interferences

Any chloride-containing compound will interfere with this determination.

1,1-Dichloro-1-Nitroethane

Jacobs, Morris B. *The Analytical Chemistry of Industrial Poisons, Hazards and Solvents,* 2nd ed. (New York: Interscience Publishers, Inc., 1949), p 737.

1,1-Dichloro-1-nitroethane, in the parts per million range, can be determined by this method. The air sample is collected in a midget impinger containing methanol. After collection, an aliquot less than 6 ml is quantitatively transferred to a 25-ml volumetric flask. The sample is cooled in a refrigerator for 1 hour. Resorcinol in methyl alcohol and sodium hydroxide is added to the sample which is then diluted to 23 ml. The sample is placed in a refrigerator for 4 hours to develop a green color. Then sulfuric acid is added to the sample and the color changes to light tan. The color is read in a spectrophotometer at a wavelength of 480 mμ. The quantity of 1,1-dichloro-1-nitroethane is read from a calibration curve, and the airborne concentration is calculated.

Sampling Procedure

The sample is collected in a midget impinger containing 10 ml of methanol. The sampling rate is 2 lpm. A suitable sample will usually be collected in 30 minutes.

This method requires approximately 6 hours for complete analysis, but most of this time is consumed in the cooling process. The method is suitable for industrial hygiene work but is not sufficiently sensitive for air pollution work.

Jones, L. R., and J. A. Reddick. **Colorimetric Determination of Nitroparaffins,** Anal. Chem. **24,** 1533 (1952).

1,1-Dichloro-1-nitroethane, in concentrations above 3 μg in the sample analyzed, can be determined by this method. The sample is collected in two fritted bubblers containing concentrated sulfuric acid. An aliquot of the sample, up to 10 ml, is quantitatively transferred to a test tube and held in a boiling water bath for 5 minutes. After cooling, resorcinol solution is placed on top of the acid and the sample is slowly mixed. It is heated in a water bath and cooled. The optical density of the resulting red-blue color is read in a spectrophotometer at a wavelength of 560 mμ. The quantity of 1,1-dichloro-1-nitroethane present is read from a calibration curve and the airborne concentration is calculated.

Sampling Procedure

The sample is collected in two bubblers, series-connected, containing sulfuric acid. A sampling rate of 2 lpm for a period long enough to collect 5–10 μg will provide an adequate sample.

Interferences

Any aliphatic nitroparaffin will interfere with this determination. The method requires approximately 30 minutes for complete analysis. It is suitable for industrial hygiene work, and, if a large enough sample is collected, it is also applicable to air pollution work.

Diethanolamine

Miller, F. A. **Determination of Diethanolamine and 2-Methylaminoethanol in Air,** Am. Ind. Hyg. Assoc. J. 29, 411 (1968).

Diethanolamine in concentrations above 0.02 ppm and 2-methylaminoethanol above 0.04 ppm, in a 25-liter air sample, can be determined by this method. An aliquot of the sample no larger than 2 ml is quantitatively transferred to a stoppered tube. Periodic acid is added to convert a portion of the amine to formaldehyde. After 10 minutes potassium arsenite and chromotropic acid are added to the sample. After being heated in a boiling water bath for 30 minutes, the sample is cooled and diluted to 20 ml. The absorbance of the resulting solution is read in a spectrophotometer at a wavelength of 570 mμ. Suitable standards are treated in the same manner.

Sampling Procedure

The sample is collected in a fritted bubbler containing 10 ml distilled water. A sampling rate of 2 lpm for a period long enough to collect a 25-liter air sample is satisfactory.

Interferences

Formaldehyde will interfere with this determination; 2-diethylamino-ethanol will not. The method ,is suitable for industrial hygiene work; complete analysis requires approximately 2 hours.

Diethylamine

Dahlgren, G. **Spectrophotometric Determination of Ethyl-Diethyl and Triethylamine in Aqueous Solution,** Anal. Chem. **36,** 596 (1964).

Diethylamine, in the parts per billion range, can be determined by this method. The samples should be collectable in distilled water in a standard impinger. A 25-ml aliquot is used for analysis. Sodium bicarbonate, hypochlorite solution, nitrite solution and standard potassium iodide are added to the sample. The absorbance of the color is read at 540 mμ in a spectrophotometer.

Sampling Procedure

The sampling rate can probably be as high as 1 cfm through the standard impinger containing 75–100 ml distilled water.

Interferences

Aniline and possibly some of the other amines interfere with the procedure. The method should require about 1 hour or less.

Hong, W. H., and K. A. Conners. **Spectrophotometric Determination of Aliphatic Amines by Acylation with Cinnamic Anhydride,** Anal. Chem. **40,** 1273 (1968).

Diethylamine, in concentrations at the parts per million level, can be determined by this method. This method was not designed specifically for air analysis but appears to be applicable. A 1-ml aliquot of the sample is quantitatively transferred to a 50-ml volumetric flask. Cinnamic anhydride solution and tri-*n*-butylamine in acetonitrile are added, mixed, and allowed to react at room temperature for several minutes. Sodium hydroxide is added to the 50-ml mark and allowed to stand for 10 minutes. The sample mixture is quantitatively transferred to a separatory funnel and extracted with chloroform. The chloroform extract is washed with distilled water and filtered into a 50-ml volumetric flask. The sample is made to volume with chloroform, and the absorbance of the sample is read in a spectrophotometer at 277 mμ. The airborne concentration of diethylamine is calculated.

Sampling Procedure

An air sampling procedure must be developed. Collection might be accomplished using a fritted bubbler containing an acetonitrile solution.

Interferences

Any aliphatic amine will interfere with this method.

2-Diethylaminoethanol

Miller, F. A., R. F. Scherberger, K. S. Tischer, and A. M. Webber. **Determination of Microgram Quantities of Diethanolamine, 2-Methylaminoethanol, and 2-Diethylaminoethanol in Air,** Am. Ind. Hyg. Assoc. J. **28**, 330 (1967).

2-Diethylaminoethanol, in concentrations above 0.01 ppm, can be determined quickly and accurately by this method. The air sample is collected in two gas washing bottles in series, each containing distilled water. An aliquot of no more than 2 ml is used for analysis. This volume is treated with ethylene dichloride. Sodium hydroxide and potassium iodide are added to the sample, which is then shaken and centrifuged. Methyl Orange is next added and the entire solution is shaken first and then centrifuged. Five ml of the resulting sample is added to a sulfuric acid–ethyl alcohol solution which is read in a spectrophotometer at 540 mμ. The amount of 2-diethylaminoethanol in the sample is read from a previously prepared calibration curve.

Sampling Procedure

The sample can be collected at a rate of 2 lpm for 30 minutes.

The method is applicable to industrial hygiene work and requires less than 2 hours for complete analysis.

4,4'-Diisocyanatodiphenylmethane

Meddle, D. W., D. W. Radford, and R. Wood. **A Field Method for the Determination of Organic Aromatic Isocyanates in Air,** Analyst 94, 369 (1969).

4,4'-Diisocyanatodiphenylmethane (MDI), in concentrations from 0.0–0.4 ppm, can be determined by this method. The sample is collected in a small fritted bubbler containing dimethylformamide in dilute hydrochloric acid. After collection, a solution of sodium nitrite and bromide, sulfamic acid and N-1-naphthylethylenediamine are added to the sample. The resulting color is compared with color standards or the absorbance is read in a spectrophotometer. The concentration of isocyanate is then calculated.

Sampling Procedure

The air sample is collected in a small bubbler at a rate of 1 lpm for 10 minutes. This procedure should provide sufficient sample for analysis.

Interferences

Other isocyanates and any primary amines will interfere with this determination.

The method requires approximately 45 minutes for complete analysis. The procedure is applicable to both industrial hygiene and air pollution work.

Dimethylamine-Borane

Hill, W. H., G. J. Levinskas, and W. J. Novick. **Iodometric Monitoring of Boron-Containing Atmospheres,** Am. Ind. Hyg. Assoc. Quart. 17, 61 (1956).

Dimethylamine-borane and other boranes, at concentrations below 0.5 ppm, can be determined with this method. A Tutwiler buret is used for sampling and analysis. The apparatus is filled with a barrier liquid of starch water, a 100 or 500 ml-air sample is aspirated, and the sample is titrated with 0.01 or 0.001N iodine depending on the required sensitivity.

Interferences

Almost all the boranes can be determined by this method. Any contaminant in the air sample that reacts with iodine will interfere.

This method is suitable for industrial hygiene work, but it is probably not sensitive enough for air pollution work. It requires approximately 1 hour for complete analysis.

2,5-Dimethylaniline

Hanson, H. W., D. A. Reilly, and H. E. Stagg, Eds. *The Determination of Toxic Substances in Air* (Cambridge, England: W. Heffer and Sons, Ltd., 1965), p 56.

2,5-Dimethylaniline, in concentrations above 1 μg per 10 ml of hydrochloric acid sampling solution, can be determined quickly and easily by this method. The sample is collected in a fritted bubbler containing 10 ml of a standardized hydrochloric acid solution. The sample is quantitatively transferred to a volumetric flask. A sodium nitrite solution is added and allowed to stand for 15 minutes at a temperature below 15°C. Sodium sulfamate, sodium acetate, N-sulfatoethyl-m-toluidine and hydrochloric acid are added. Full color development occurs in 1.5 hours. The optical density of the solution is read on a spectrophotometer at a wavelength of 500 mμ. The quantity of 2,5-dimethylaniline present is determined from a previously prepared calibration curve, and the airborne concentration is calculated.

The sampling rate through the fritted bubbler should be approximately 5 lpm. The duration of sampling depends on the expected concentration of the amine.

Interferences

Many amines and their derivatives interfere with this method. The method is relatively simple and requires about 2 hours for complete analysis. No special or expensive equipment is required. The method is suitable for industrial hygiene work.

1,1-Dimethylhydrazine

Pinkerton, M. K., J. M. Lauer, P. Diamond, and A. A. Tamas. A Colorimetric Determination for 1,1-Dimethylhydrazine (UDMH) in Air,
Blood and Water, Am. Ind. Hyg. Assoc. J. **24,** 239 (1963).

1,1-Dimethylhydrazine (UDMH), in concentrations from 2.5–50 ppm,
can be determined with this method. The range can be extended by
proper dilution techniques. The sample is collected in a polyethylene
bubbler containing a buffer solution citric acid and disodium phosphate
in water. Trisodium pentacyanoamino ferroate is added to an aliquot of
the sample. The resulting red-orange color is allowed to develop for
1 hour and the optical density at 500 mμ is determined with a spectrophotometer. The concentration is determined by comparison with a
standard curve and the airborne concentration is calculated.

Sampling Procedures

The sampling rate through the bubbler can be 1 lpm for 2 minutes.
Longer sampling times can be used but the sample must be diluted to
fall into the range of the determination.

Interferences

Nitrogen dioxide may interfere with the determination by somewhat
reducing the color produced.

This method is applicable to industrial hygiene analysis and requires
2–3 hours for a complete analysis. The method is not sensitive enough
for air pollution work.

Epichlorohydrin

Hanson, N. W., D. A. Reilly, and H. E. Stagg, Eds. *The Determination of Toxic Substances in Air* (Cambridge, England: W. Heffer and
Sons, Ltd., 1965), p 121.

See Also

1. Nash, T.   Biochem. J. **55,** 416 (1953).
2. Gage, J. C.   Brit. J. Ind. Med. **16,** 11 (1959).

Epichlorohydrin, in concentrations from 2.5–20 ppm in a 1-liter air
sample, can be determined by this method. The air sample is collected

in two midget impingers containing 8 ml of water and connected in series. After collection, the sample is heated for 1 hour to open the epoxide ring, producing glycerol chlorohydrin which is then oxidized with periodic acid to produce formaldehyde. Sodium arsenite and a solution of acetylacetone in acetic acid and ammonium acetate is added to the sample and heated for several minutes. The optical density of the resulting yellow-stained solution is read in a spectrophotometer at 412 mμ. The quantity of epichlorohydrin present in the sample is read from a previously prepared calibration curve and the airborne concentration is calculated.

Sampling Procedure

The sampling rate through the two midget impingers should be approximately 1 lpm. If 1 liter of air is sampled, the method can be expected to determine 2.5–20 ppm. An increase or decrease in the sampling time will provide an increase or decrease of the sensitivity limits obtainable.

Interferences

Formaldehyde, other aldehydes, and substances yielding aldehydes when exposed to the reagents used in this analysis can be expected to interfere with this determination.

The method is simple and requires approximately 3 hours for complete analysis. It is applicable to industrial hygiene work but is not considered sufficiently sensitive for air pollution work.

Daniel, J. W., and J. C. Gage. **The Determination of Epichlorohydrin in Air,** Analyst 81, 594 (1956).

Epichlorohydrin, in concentrations above 10 mg/m^3, can be determined by this method. The sample is collected in a specially constructed bubbler containing 8 ml distilled water. The sample is diluted to 10 ml with distilled water and quantitatively transferred to a flask. Periodic acid is added and the solution heated in a water bath for 20 minutes. Arsenite solution and a solution consisting of a mixture of ammonium acetate, glacial acetic acid and acetylacetone are added to the sample. The optical density of the resulting stained solution is read in a spectrophotometer at a wavelength of 412 mμ.

Sampling Procedure

The sample is collected in a specially constructed bubbler containing 8 ml of distilled water. A sampling rate of 0.5 lpm for 5 minutes will usually provide an adequate sample.

Interferences

Formaldehyde, formaldehyde-producing substances, ethylene oxide, and ethylene glycol will interfere with this determination. The method requires less than 2 hours for analysis and is suitable for industrial hygiene work. It is not sufficiently sensitive for air pollution work.

Ethyl Acetate

Goddu, R. F., N. F. Le Blanc, and C. M. Wright. **Spectrophotometric Determination of Esters and Anhydrides by Hydroxamic Acid Reaction,** Anal. Chem. **27,** 1251 (1955).

See Also

Hill, V. T.   Ind. Eng. Chem., Anal. Ed. **18,** 317 (1946).

Ethyl acetate, in concentrations above approximately 20 ppm in a 25-liter air sample, can be determined by this method. The sample is collected in two fritted bubblers connected in series, each containing ethyl alcohol. The sample is reacted with an alkaline hydroxylamine solution. The addition of ferric ion to this mixture produces a highly-colored product. The absorbance of this product is read at a wavelength of 530 mμ, and the quantity of ester present is read from a calibration curve. The airborne concentration is calculated.

Sampling Procedure

The air sample is collected in two fritted bubblers connected in series, each containing 10 ml ethyl alcohol. The sampling rate should be approximately 1–2 lpm until at least 25 liters of air have been sampled.

Interferences

Any other ester, anhydrides, aldehydes, and isocyanates will interfere with this determination.

This method requires approximately 2 hours for complete analysis. The method is applicable to industrial hygiene work but is not sufficiently sensitive for air pollution work.

Hanson, N. W., D. A. Reilly, and H. E. Stagg, Eds. *The Determination of Toxic Substances in Air* (Cambridge, England: W. Heffer and Sons, Ltd., 1965), p 37.

See Also

Hestrin, S. J. J. Biol. Chem. **180,** 249 (1949).

Ethyl acetate, in concentrations from 10–400 ppm, can be determined quickly and accurately by this method. The sample is collected in an impinger containing ethyl alcohol. It is quantitatively transferred to a volumetric flask and a solution of hydroxylammonium chloride is added. Following this, sodium hydroxide, hydrochloric acid and ferric chloride are added to the sample. The sample is then diluted to 25 ml with water and allowed to stand for 30 minutes. The optical density of the resulting purple solution is read in a spectrophotometer at 510 mμ.

The sampling rate should be approximately 0.5 lpm, and approximately 0.6 liters of air should be sampled to provide the sensitivity stated above. Increasing or decreasing the volume of air sampled will increase or decrease the concentration range to which this method is applicable.

Interferences

Methyl, butyl and isoamyl acetate will interfere with this analysis. The anhydrides and chlorides of carboxylic acids also interfere with this determination.

The method is simple, takes approximately 1.5 hours to complete and requires no special or expensive equipment. It is suitable for industrial hygiene work but is not sufficiently sensitive for air pollution work.

Ethyl Acrylate

Gisclard, J. B., D. B. Robinson, and P. J. Kuczy. **A Rapid Empirical Procedure for the Determination of Acrylonitrile and Acrylic Esters in the Atmosphere,** Am. Ind. Hyg. Assoc. J. 19:43 (1958).

Ethyl acrylate, in concentrations above 10 ppm, can be determined by this method. The air sample is collected in a midget impinger equipped with a specially constructed suction device. Any suction device can be used provided a flow rate of 300 ml can be maintained through the impinger. The impinger contains potassium permanganate, sodium hydroxide and telluric acid. A 200-ml air sample is pulled through the impinger and sampling solution in 20 seconds. The air sample is collected in this same manner until the permanganate changes color from pink to bluish-green. The concentration of solvent is then determined from a calibration curve showing air volume versus parts per million.

Interferences

Any compound containing double-bonded carbon atoms may interfere with this determination.

The method is suitable for industrial hygiene field work but is empirical in nature; judgment must be exercised when basing recommendations on data provided by this analysis. The method requires about 30 minutes for completion.

Ethyl Alcohol

Williams, M. B., and H. D. Relse. **Colorimetric Determination of Ethyl Alcohol,** Anal. Chem. 22, 1556 (1950).

Ethyl alcohol, in concentrations above approximately 1 μg per ml of solution, can be determined by this method. A 10-ml sample is quantitatively transferred to a test tube and a dichromate solution is added. After heating, the sample is diluted to 2 liters in a volumetric flask. A 10-ml aliquot of this solution is reacted with sulfuric acid and s-diphenylcarbazide and diluted to 100 ml. The resulting violet-colored solution is read in a spectrophotometer at a wavelength of 540 mμ.

Sampling Procedure

This method is applicable to industrial hygiene work even though it was not designed for air analysis. The sample could be collected in midget impingers, fritted bubblers or standard impingers at appropriate flow rates.

Interferences

Any oxidizable compound as well as other alcohols interfere with this determination. Molybdenum, mercury, iron, and vanadium may also interfere. The method requires less than 1 hour for completion and is sufficiently sensitive for industrial hygiene work.

Hanson, N. W., D. A. Reilly, and H. E. Stagg, Eds. *The Determination of Toxic Substances in Air* (Cambridge, England: W. Heffer and Sons, Ltd., 1965), p 125.

Ethyl alcohol, in concentrations from 50–5000 ppm in a 5-liter air sample, can be determined by this method. The air sample is collected in a midget impinger containing 10 ml distilled water. It is quantitatively transferred to a volumetric flask and diluted to 50 ml with water. One-half the sample is then transferred to an Erlenmeyer flask and an accurately measured volume of a standardized solution of potassium dichromate is added. The sample is cooled in an ice bath and concentrated sulfuric acid is slowly added. The entire solution is placed in the dark for 1 hour. The same procedure is carried out on a blank. After 1 hour, water, potassium iodide and a copper sulfate solution of known concentration are added to the sample. The liberated iodine is titrated with a standard thiosulfate solution. The blank is treated in the same way. The quantity of ethyl alcohol present is equal to the difference in volume of sodium thiosulfate used in the blank and in the sample.

The sampling rate through the midget impinger containing water should be approximately 1.5 lpm. A sample volume of 5 liters will produce an analytical range of 50–5000 ppm.

Interferences

The method is not specific for ethyl alcohol, and any oxidizable compound will interfere with the analysis.

The method is simple and requires approximately 1.5 hours for completion. No special or expensive equipment is required and the method is suitable for industrial hygiene work.

Hoare, D. E., and R. R. Ogilvie. **Spectrophotometric Method for the Microdetermination of Monohydric Aliphatic Alcohols,** Anal. Chem. **38,** 1799 (1966).

This method was not designed for air analysis but appears to be applicable for this use. Ethyl alcohol, in concentrations exceeding 0.1 μg per ml, can be determined by this method. The sample is collected in a midget impinger containing water. An 8-ml aliquot of the sample along with an acetate buffer and sodium nitrite solution are quantitatively transferred to a 50-ml flask.

The sample is incubated at 18°C for 30 minutes, after which heptane is added. The entire sample is again incubated at 18°C and agitated. It is cooled at 0°C and transferred to a cold separatory funnel; the aqueous layer is removed. The heptane layer is transferred to a test tube and exposed to calcium chloride to remove the water. The sample is reacted with α-naphthylamine and incubated at 18°C for 10 minutes. The color is allowed to develop while the sample is contained in a water bath at 60°C for 30 minutes. After cooling, the absorbance of the resulting solution is read in a spectrophotometer at 550 mμ. The concentration present in the sample is read from a calibration curve, and airborne concentration is calculated.

Sampling Procedure

The sample is collected by a fritted bubbler at a rate of 2 lpm. Water may be used as the sampling solution.

Interferences

The method is not specific for monohydric aliphatic alcohols but determines many of them. It requires approximately 3 hours for complete analysis and is suitable for industrial hygiene work.

Jaselskis, B., and J. P. Warriner. **Titrimetric Determination of Primary and Secondary Alcohols by Xenon Trioxide Oxidation,** Anal. Chem. 38, 563 (1966).

Ethyl alcohol, in concentrations above 30 μg, can be determined by this method. An aliquot of the sample containing at least 30 μg of alcohol is quantitatively transferred to an Erlenmeyer flask. The sample is diluted to 20 ml and a known quantity of xenon trioxide standard solution is added. After 2 hours, several drops of sulfuric acid and sodium iodide are added to liberate the triiodide ion. The quantity of xenon trioxide used during the oxidation equals the difference between the xenon trioxide before reaction and after reaction with the alcohol. The quantity of alcohol present is determined from a calibration curve, and the airborne concentration is calculated.

Sampling Procedure

The sample is collected in a fritted bubbler containing distilled water at a rate of 2.8 lpm for a period long enough to collect 30 μg.

Interferences

Halides, amines, carboxylic acids, ketones, and aldehydes interfere with this determination.

The method requires approximately 4 hours for complete analysis. It is suitable for industrial hygiene analysis but is probably not sensitive enough for air pollution work.

Ethyl Mercaptan

Moore, H., H. L. Helwig, and R. J. Grave. **A Spectrophotometer Method for the Determination of Mercaptans in Air,** Am. Ind. Hyg. J. **21,** 466 (1960).

Ethyl mercaptan, in concentrations above 0.5 ppm in a 1-liter air sample, can be rapidly and accurately determined by this method. The air sample is collected in a fritted bubbler containing mercuric acetate solution. The sample is placed in a volumetric flask and diluted with distilled water. N,N-Dimethyl-p-phenylenediamine in hydrochloric acid and ferric chloride in nitric acid solution are added to the sample. The resulting red color is allowed to develop for 30 minutes and read in a spectrophotometer at 500 mμ. Standards are prepared from lead methyl mercaptide.

Sampling Procedure

Sampling rates of less than 0.5 lpm for a fritted bubbler and 1.5 lpm for a large bubbler are satisfactory for collection of the mercaptan. A 30-minute sample is usually adequate.

Interferences

The method is not specific for any one mercaptan and all mercaptans will interfere. Hydrogen sulfide, sulfur dioxide, and nitrogen dioxide do not interfere at the concentrations usually found in air pollution or industrial hygiene studies.

This method is applicable to both industrial hygiene and air pollution work. It requires about 2 hours for completion.

Ethylamine

Scherberger, R. F., F. H. Miller, and D. W. Fasset. **The Determination of N-Butylamine in Air,** Am. Ind. Hyg. Assoc. J. **21,** 471 (1960).

Ethylamine, in concentrations above 0.1 ppm in a 1-cubic foot air sample, can be determined by this method. The air sample is collected in a gas washing bottle or midget fritted bubbler containing a solution of concentrated hydrochloric acid and isopropyl alcohol. An aliquot of less than 3 ml is used for analysis. Pyridine and ninhydrin in isopropyl alcohol are added to the sample which is then heated in a water bath for 7 minutes. The sample is next cooled for 10 minutes in a cold water bath. The absorbance of the resulting solution is read in a spectrophotometer at 575 mμ. The concentration of ethylamine in the sample is determined from a calibration curve, and the airborne concentration is calculated.

Sampling Procedure

A sampling rate of 0.1 cfm for periods ranging upwards of 10 minutes is satisfactory for collection of the amine if a fritted midget bubbler is used.

Interferences

The method is not specific for any one amine and other amines will interfere.

The determination is simple and rapid, requiring approximately 2 hours for completion. The method is applicable to industrial hygiene work and in some cases to air pollution analysis.

Dahlgren, G. **Spectrophotometric Determination of Ethyl–Diethyl and Triethylamine in Aqueous Solution,** Anal. Chem. **36,** 596 (1964).

Ethylamine, in the parts per billion range, can be determined by this method. The samples are collectable in distilled water in a standard impinger. A 25-ml aliquot is used for analysis. Sodium bicarbonate, hypochlorite solution, nitrite solution and standard potassium iodide are added to the sample. The absorbance of the color is read at 540 mμ in a spectrophotometer.

Sampling Procedure

The sampling rate can probably be as high as 1 cubic foot per minute through the standard impinger containing 75–100 ml distilled water.

Interferences

Aniline and possibly some of the other amines interfere with the procedure. The method should require about 1 hour or less.

Ethylbenzene

Jacobs, Morris B. *The Analytical Chemistry of Industrial Poisons, Hazards and Solvents,* 2nd ed. (New York: Interscience Publishers, Inc., 1949), p 546.

See Also
1. Schrenk, H. H., S. J. Pearce, and W. P. Yant. U.S. Bur. Mines, Rept. Invest. **3287** (1935).
2. Pearce, S. J., H. H. Schrenk, and W. P. Yant. U.S. Bur. Mines, Rept. Invest. **3302** (1936).

Ethylbenzene, in concentrations above 25 ppm, can be determined by this method if a 0.5-liter air sample is collected. This limit can be extended by increasing the sampling time significantly. The air sample is collected by sampling through a special bubbler containing a nitrating acid composed of equal quantities of concentrated sulfuric acid and fuming nitric acid. After collection, the sample is allowed to react for 30 minutes to ensure that nitration is complete. The sample is quantitatively transferred to an Erlenmeyer flask and cooled below 20°C. The sample is then neutralized by adding sodium hydroxide slowly and carefully. The solution is warmed to 30°C, and 10 ml of methyl ethyl ketone (butanone) are added. The sample is transferred to a separatory funnel and the water drawn off. Sodium hydroxide is added and the color is allowed to develop for 1 hour. The resulting green color is compared with a set of standards and the quantity present in the sample is determined. The airborne concentration is calculated.

Sampling Procedure

The sample may be collected in a special bubbler containing nitrating acid. A sampling rate of 30 ml per minute for approximately 1 hour should provide a sufficient sample for analysis.

Interferences

Toluene, benzene, chlorobenzene, styrene and xylene will interfere with this determination.

The method requires approximately 3 hours for completion. If a 60-minute sample is collected, the method is suitable for industrial hygiene work but is not sufficiently sensitive for air pollution work.

Yamamoto, R. K., and W. A. Cook. **Determination of Ethylbenzene and Styrene in Air by Ultraviolet Spectrophotometry,** Am. Ind. Hyg. Assoc. J. **29,** 238 (1968).

Ethylbenzene and styrene in the presence of each other can be determined by ultraviolet spectroscopy. The sample is collected in a midget impinger, containing isooctane, for 10 minutes. Ethylbenzene is determined at a wavelength of 268 mμ while styrene is determined at a wavelength of 291 mμ.

Results indicate that styrene can be collected with an efficiency of 90% if the airborne concentration is above 25 ppm. Ethylbenzene can be collected with an 80% efficiency if the airborne concentration is above 50 ppm, provided that the concentration is equal to or greater than the concentration of styrene.

Ethylene Chlorohydrin

Jacobs, Morris B. *The Analytical Chemistry of Industrial Poisons, Hazards and Solvents,* 2nd ed. (New York: Interscience Publishers, Inc., 1949), p 611.

Ethylene chlorohydrin, in concentrations greater than 1 ppm, can be determined by this method. The sample is collected in two fritted bubblers in series containing a potassium hydroxide solution. After collection, the sample is quantitatively transferred to a refluxing flask and refluxed for 1 hour. The sample is acidified with nitric acid and the liberated chloride is titrated with a standardized silver nitrate solution using potassium chromate as the indicator. The concentration of ethylene chlorohydrin is calculated.

Sampling Procedure

The sample is collected in two fritted bubblers connected in series containing 10 ml of potassium hydroxide solution at a rate of 1 lpm. A 30-minute procedure should collect an adequate sample.

Interferences

Any chloride will interfere with this determination.

The method requires approximately 2 hours for completion. It is suitable for industrial hygiene but is not sufficiently sensitive for air pollution work.

Hanson, N. W., D. A. Reilly, and H. E. Stagg, Eds. *The Determination of Toxic Substances in Air* (Cambridge, England: W. Heffer and Sons., Ltd., 1965), p 126.

Ethylene chlorohydrin, in concentrations from 0.6–12.0 ppm in a 50-liter air sample, can be determined by this method. The air sample is collected in a small gas washing bottle containing 20 ml pyridine solution. After collection, the sample is quantitatively transferred to an Erlenmeyer flask, methyl alcohol is added, and the sample is heated in a water bath. Acetic acid is added, the solution is heated, and then the optical density is read at 415 mμ in a spectrophotometer. The quantity of ethylene chlorohydrin is read from a previously prepared calibration curve, and the airborne concentration is calculated.

The sampling rate through the gas washing bottle should be approximately 1 lpm.

Interferences

Chlorine interferes with the determination at concentrations in excess of 3 ppm. Ethylene dichloride, carbon tetrachloride, trichloroethylene, and chloroform do not interfere.

The method is simple and requires approximately 1.5 hours for complete analysis. No special or expensive equipment is required, and the method is suitable for industrial hygiene work.

Ethylene Dibromide

Jacobs, Morris B. *The Analytical Chemistry of Industrial Poisons, Hazards and Solvents,* 2nd ed. (New York: Interscience Publishers, Inc., 1949), p 606.

See Also
1. Brenner, W. M., and G. L. Poland.   Ind. Eng. Chem., Anal. Ed. **10,** 528 (1938).
2. Dillon, R. T.   J. Am. Chem. Soc. **54,** 952 (1932).

Ethylene dibromide, in the parts per million range, can be determined by this method. The sample is collected in a midget impinger containing alcohol. An aliquot of the sample is quantitatively transferred to an Erlenmeyer flask, and potassium iodide and alcohol are added. This mixture is refluxed for 3 hours, cooled, diluted with distilled water, and the iodine is titrated with a standardized thiosulfate solution. The airborne concentration of ethylene dibromide is calculated.

Sampling Procedure

A midget bubbler containing 10 ml or a gas washing bottle containing 50 ml of a potassium iodide solution can be used to collect the sample. A 30-minute sample at least should be collected at a rate appropriate for the particular sample used.

Interferences

Any material reacting with potassium iodide producing iodine will interfere with this determination.

The method requires approximately 4 hours for completion. The technique is suitable for industrial hygiene work but is not sufficiently sensitive for air pollution work.

Ethylene Dichloride

Hanson, N. W., D. A. Reilly, and H. E. Stagg, Eds. *The Determination of Toxic Substances in Air* (Cambridge, England: W. Heffer and Sons, Ltd., 1965), p 103.

Ethylene dichloride (1,2-dichloroethane), in concentrations from 25–250 ppm in a 1-liter air sample, can be determined by this method. The air sample is collected in a midget impinger containing 10 ml of an aqueous pyridine solution. The sample is quantitatively transferred to a flask and heated in a water bath for 15 minutes. After cooling, a known volume of a standard sodium hydroxide is added to the sample which is then diluted to 30 ml with ethyl alcohol. The optical density of the sample is read in a spectrophotometer at a wavelength of 415 mμ. The quantity of ethylene chloride present in the sample is read from a previously prepared calibration curve, and the airborne concentration of the material is calculated.

The sampling rate through the impinger containing pyridine should be approximately 0.5 lpm. A 1-liter sample will produce a sensitivity range of 25–250 ppm. Increasing or decreasing the volume of air sampled will increase or decrease the upper and lower values. This sampling system provides a sampling efficiency of only 80%. This must be considered in concentration calculations.

Interferences

Carbon tetrachloride, chloroform, trichloroethylene, and ethylene chlorohydrin do not interfere with the analysis. Chlorine in concentrations exceeding 3 ppm will interfere.

The method is simple and rapid, requiring about 30 minutes to complete the analysis. No special or expensive equipment is required. This method is suitable for industrial hygiene work, but it is not considered sufficiently sensitive for air pollution work.

Ethyl Formate

Goddu, R. F., N. F. LeBlanc, and C. M. Wright. **Spectrophotometric Determination of Esters and Anhydrides by Hydroxamic Acid Reaction,** Anal. Chem. **27,** 1253 (1955).

This method is not designed for air analysis but could be modified to be applicable. Ethyl formate is converted to a hydroxamic acid by reaction with hydroxylamine in alkaline solution. The acid produces a colored complex with ferric ion which can be read in a spectrophotometer at a wavelength from 550–560 mμ.

Interferences

Acid chlorides, carbonyls, copper, nickel, vanadium, chloride, tartrate and acetic acid interfere with this determination.

Ethylenimine

Epstein, J., R. W. Rosenthal, and R. J. Ess. **Use of γ-(4-Nitrobenzyl) Pyridine as Analytical Reagent for Ethylenimines and Alkylating Agents,** Anal. Chem. **27,** 1435 (1955).

Ethylenimine, in the parts per million range, can be determined by this method. The sample might be collected in one or two fritted bubblers connected in series, containing 0.01*M* potassium acid phthalate. A 4-ml aliquot of the sample is quantitatively transferred to a test tube. Clark and Lubs pH 4.0 buffer solution and γ-(4-nitrobenzyl) pyridine are added, and the sample is heated in a water bath and cooled in an ice bath. Acetone and potassium carbonate are added and the absorbance of the resulting solution is read at a wavelength of 600 mμ. The quantity of ethylenimine in the aliquot is read from a calibration curve, and the airborne concentration is calculated.

Sampling Procedure

The sample is collected in one or two fritted bubblers containing potassium acid phthalate. A sampling rate of 2.8 lpm should be adequate.

The method requires less than 1 hour for completion. It is applicable to both industrial hygiene and air pollution work.

Crompton, T. R. **Determination of Traces of Ethylenimine Monomer in Samples of Air,** Analyst **90,** 107 (1965).

Ethylenimine, in concentrations above 1 ppm, can be determined by this method. The sample is collected in a 250-ml fritted bubbler protected from light. After collection, the sample is quantitatively transferred to a separatory funnel, also protected from light. The sample is extracted with chloroform. The optical density of the resulting orange-colored solution is read in a spectrophotometer at a wavelength of 420 mμ. The quantity of ethylenimine present is read from a calibration curve, and the airborne concentration is calculated.

Sampling Procedure

The sample is collected in a 250-ml fritted glass bubbler containing a solution of sodium 1,2-naphthoquinone-4-sulfonate and enough phosphate buffer to provide a pH of 10.1.   mpling rate of approximately 0.1 lpm is adequate.

Interferences

There are no known interferences with this method.

The method requires approximately 2 hours for complete analysis. It is suitable for industrial hygiene work but is not sufficiently sensitive for air pollution work.

Ethylene Oxide

Jacobs, Morris B. *The Analytical Chemistry of Industrial Poisons, Hazards and Solvents,* 2nd ed. (New York: Interscience Publishers, Inc., 1949), p 649.

Ethylene oxide, in the parts per million range, can be determined by this method. The sample is collected in a fritted bubbler containing a standardized hydrochloric acid solution. The sample is then titrated with a standardized barium hydroxide solution using Methyl Orange as indicator, and the airborne ethylene oxide concentration is calculated.

Sampling Procedure

A fritted bubbler containing a standardized solution of hydrochloric acid can be used to collect the sample at a rate of approximately 2 lpm. A sampling duration of 30 minutes is usually sufficient.

Interferences

Any acidic material will interfere with this determination.

The method requires approximately 1 hour for complete determination. It is suitable for industrial hygiene work but is not sufficiently sensitive for air pollution work.

Gunther, F. A., and R. C. Blinn. *Analysis of Insecticides and Acaricides* (New York: Interscience Publishers, Inc., 1955).

See Also

El Khishen, S. A.   J. Sci. Food Agr. 1, 71 (1950).

Ethylene oxide, in concentrations in the parts per million range, can be determined rapidly and accurately by this method. The air sample is collected in three fritted bubblers in series. The first two bubblers are charged with a solution of hydrochloric acid and magnesium chloride while the third is charged with standard sodium hydroxide. Following sample collection, the solutions in the bubblers are quantitatively transferred to a flask. Excess standard sodium hydroxide is titrated with standard hydrochloric acid solution using Methyl Orange as the indicator.

The sampling rate for collection of ethylene oxide should be about 300 ml per minute for a long enough time to collect several mg of ethylene oxide.

Interferences

Any material which is either acidic or basic will interfere with this method. The determination is simple and rapid, requiring no special or expensive equipment. It is suitable for industrial hygiene work and for the analysis of ethylene oxide as an airborne pesticide. The method is not sensitive enough for general air pollution work. Analysis requires approximately 1 hour for completion.

Hanson, N. W., D. A. Reilly, and H. E. Stagg, Eds. *The Determination of Toxic Substances in Air* (Cambridge, England: W. Heffer and Sons, Ltd., 1965), p 128.

See Also

Gage, J. C.   Analyst **82**, 587 (1957).

Ethylene oxide, in concentrations from 0–110 ppm in a 0.25-liter air sample, can be determined by this method. The air sample is collected in a midget impinger containing 10 ml distilled water. It is quantitatively transferred to a 20-ml volumetric flask. Periodic acid is added to the sample and the solution is heated in a water bath. A solution of acetylacetone in acetic acid containing ammonium acetate is added to the sample. A sodium arsenate solution is added and the optical density of the resulting yellow color is read in a spectrophotometer at a wavelength of 412 mμ. The quantity of ethylene oxide in the sample is determined from a previously prepared calibration curve, and the airborne concentration is calculated. The sampling rate through the impinger should be approximately 0.5 lpm.

Interferences

Formaldehyde and ethylene glycol will interfere with this method.

The method is simple and rapid, requiring approximately 2 hours to complete the analysis. No special equipment is required. This method is suitable for industrial hygiene work, and it also appears to be sensitive enough for air pollution work.

Fluoride

Hensley, A. L., and J. E. Braney, II.   **Spectrophotometric Determination of Fluoride with Thorium Chloranilate**, Anal. Chem. **32**, 828 (1960).

Fluorides, in concentrations above 0.01 ppm fluoride, can be quantitatively determined by this method. The fluoride should be collectable in distilled water in a midget impinger. Two procedures are described, one having a range of 0–0.2 mg fluoride, the other a range of 0.2–10 mg fluoride. The collected sample is placed in a volumetric flask and methyl Cellosolve along with a sodium acetate–acetic acid buffer are added. Thorium chloranilate is added and the mixture is shaken intermittently for 30 minutes and filtered. For higher concentrations, the absorbance is read at a wavelength of 540 mμ while lower concentrations are read at a wavelength of 330 mμ.

Sampling Procedure

A sampling rate of about 0.1 cfm in a midget impinger containing 10 ml of distilled water should be adequate for sample collection. A sampling duration of 30 minutes will usually collect an adequate sample.

Interferences

Cations interfere with the determination but most of them can be removed by ion-exchange resins. Aluminum and zinc are not removed by ion exchange and, if present, must be separated from the fluoride by distillation. Anions that interfere include phosphate, molybdate, citrate and tartrate. If these ions are present, a distillation procedure must be used to remove them.

These procedures should be applicable to the determination of airborne fluorine provided that the fluorine is converted to fluoride before analysis. Analysis requires about 1 hour.

Caley, E. R., and G. R. Kahle. **Determination of Fluorine as Lithium Fluoride,** Anal. Chem. **31,** 1880 (1959).

Fluorine, present as fluoride in aqueous solution, can be determined in the range of 20–200 mg by this method. The fluorine is collected in a midget impinger containing 10 ml distilled water. The sample is brought to a volume of 15–40 ml depending on the amount of fluoride thought to be present. The sample is heated to 70°C and an equal volume of lithium chloride in ethyl alcohol is slowly added. After cooling, the resulting precipitate is filtered through a weighed filter crucible and washed with lithium fluoride until all traces of chloride are removed. The precipitate is dried and weighed and the amount of fluoride is calculated.

Sampling Procedure

The sampling rate using the midget impinger and 10 ml of distilled water can be about 0.1 cfm.

Interferences

Fluorides interfere but sulfates interfere only slightly. Interferences of other anions was not studied.

In order to be applicable to air pollution and industrial hygiene work, the sample size must be great enough to ensure that at least 20 mg of fluoride are present. The primary application of this method is in the sampling of stack gases.

Formaldehyde

Barnes, E. C., and H. W. Speicher.   **Determination of Formaldehyde in Air,** J. Ind. Hyg. Toxicol. **24,** 10 (1942).

Formaldehyde, in concentrations above 0.005 mg in a 5-ml aliquot, can be determined by this method. The air sample is collected in a dilute potassium hydroxide solution contained in a standard impinger. A 5-ml aliquot of the sample is used for analysis. Phenylhydrazine hydrochloride, concentrated hydrochloric acid, and potassium ferricyanide are added to the neutralized sample. The absorbance of the resulting pink color is read in a spectrophotometer, and the concentration is determined from a calibration curve.

Sampling Procedure

The air sample is collected at a rate of 1 cfm for 10–30 minutes depending on the expected formaldehyde concentration.

Interferences

Acetaldehyde, acrolein and possibly other aldehydes will interfere.

The method is suitable for industrial hygiene analysis and could also be used for stack gas analysis.

Goldman, F. H., and H. Yagoda.   **Collection and Estimation of Traces of Formaldehyde in Air,** Ind. Eng. Chem., Anal. Ed. **15,** 377 (1943).

Formaldehyde, in concentrations above 0.5 mg per 10 ml absorbing solution, can be determined by this method. The air sample is collected either in a midget impinger containing 10 ml of a sodium bisulfite absorbing solution or in a standard impinger containing 100 ml of the absorbing solution. This produces a stable, nonvolatile sodium formaldehyde–bisulfite complex. A 10-ml portion of sample is used for analysis. The sample is titrated to a blue starch end point to destroy the excess bisulfite. Excess iodine is destroyed with sodium thiosulfate. Sodium carbonate reagent is added to the sample to decompose the formaldehyde–bisulfite complex. A final titration with iodine is conducted, and the quantity of formaldehyde is calculated.

Sampling Procedure

The sampling rate through the midget impinger is 1–3 lpm and 28 lpm through the standard impinger. Sampling duration depends upon expected concentration. Assuming an airborne concentration of 20 ppm, a good rule of thumb is to sample 20 liters of air for each 10 ml of bisulfite solution in the impinger.

Interferences

Acetone interferes with the analysis. The interference can be removed by adding sodium bicarbonate before the final iodometric titration.

The method is applicable to industrial hygiene analysis and to other areas where relatively high concentrations of formaldehyde might be expected. It can be applied to ambient air sampling if long sampling durations are used.

This method determines total aldehydes and not formaldehyde alone.

Jacobs, Morris B. *The Analytical Chemistry of Industrial Poisons, Hazards and Solvents,* 2nd ed. (New York: Interscience Publishers, Inc., 1949), p 686.
See Also
Morasco, M. Ind. Eng. Chem. **18**, 701 (1926).

Formaldehyde, in the parts per million range, can be determined by this method. The sample is collected in two bubblers connected in series containing hydroxylamine hydrochloride solution. The solutions in the two bubblers are combined and titrated with a standardized sodium hydroxide solution. Because more acid is released by the sample after each titration, the titration is repeated three or four times. When no more acid is liberated, the airborne concentration of formaldehyde is calculated.

Sampling Procedure

The sample is collected in two gas washing bottles containing 50 ml hydroxylamine hydrochloride solution. A sampling rate of 0.4 lpm for 30 minutes will usually collect a suitable sample.

Interferences

Acetone and possibly some of the other ketones will interfere.

The method requires approximately 1 hour for complete analysis. It is suitable for industrial hygiene work but is not sufficiently sensitive for air pollution work.

Ruch, J. E., and J. B. Johnson. **Determination of Aldehydes by Mercurimetric Oxidation,** Anal. Chem. **28,** 69 (1956).

Formaldehyde, in the parts per million range, can be determined by this method. This method is not designed for air analysis, and a sampling procedure must be devised. The sample is quantitatively transferred to an Erlenmeyer flask, at which time 50 ml of a solution of potassium iodide in potassium hydroxide is added. The sample is kept cool in an ice bath. Then 50 ml of agar and 25 ml of glacial acetic acid are added. A standardized iodine solution is then added, and after 15 minutes the sample is titrated with standardized thiosulfate solution. The quantity of aldehyde present is then calculated.

Sampling Procedure

No air sampling procedure has yet been developed.

Interferences

Alcohol and esters interfere slightly with this determination. Some vinyl compounds, unsaturated aldehydes, acetone, and methyl ethyl ketone also interfere slightly.

Jacobs, Morris B.   *The Chemical Analysis of Air Pollutants* (New York: Interscience Publishers, Inc., 1960), p 265.

See Also
1. Kersey, R. W., J. R. Maddocks, and T. E. Johnson.   Analyst **65,** 203 (1940).
2. Barnes, E. C., and H. W. Speicher.   J. Ind. Hyg. Toxicol. **24,** 10 (1942).

Formaldehyde, in the parts per million range, can be determined by this method. The sample is collected in a fritted bubbler containing 10 ml phenylhydrazine hydrochloride. After collection, the sample is diluted 10–50 ml with distilled water; a 10-ml aliquot is transferred to a Nessler tube. Hydrochloric acid and potassium ferricyanide are added and the sample is diluted to 20 ml with distilled water. The resulting red-to-violet color is compared with a set of standards prepared in a similar manner, and the airborne concentration of formaldehyde in air is calculated.

Sampling Procedure

The air sample is collected in a midget impinger containing 10 ml phenylhydrazine hydrochloride. A sampling rate of approximately 0.2 lpm is adequate for sample collection. The sample duration should be such that 1 mg of formaldehyde is collected. No more than a 40-liter sample should be collected.

Interferences

This method is relatively specific for formaldehyde.

Analysis requires approximately 1 hour to complete. This analytical technique can be used in industrial hygiene work but is not considered sensitive enough for air pollution work.

Rayner, A. G., and C. M. Jephcott. **Microdetermination of Formaldehyde in Air,** Anal. Chem. 33, 627 (1961).

Formaldehyde, in concentrations to 0.1 μg per ml of collecting solution, can be determined by this method. The air sample is collected in a standard impinger containing slightly acidified (HCl) distilled water. The collection efficiency of the solution is 72% $\pm$ 5%. An aliquot of this solution is placed in a 25-ml volumetric flask. Acetone and Schiff's reagent are added to the sample. The color is allowed to develop for at least 3 hours but preferably overnight. The absorbance of the resulting magenta color is read at 560 mμ on a spectrophotometer, and the quantity of formaldehyde present is read from a standard curve.

Sampling Procedure

A sampling rate of 1 cfm through 60–75 ml of solution contained in a standard impinger is recommended. A 30-minute sampling duration will usually collect a suitable sample.

Interferences

Acrolein, high concentrations of sulfur dioxide, and to a slight extent the oxides of nitrogen interfere.

The method is applicable to the determination of formaldehyde in air and combustion processes. It requires approximately 4 hours for complete analysis.

Kwan, T. W., and B. M. Watts. **A New Color Reaction of Anthrone with Malonaldehyde and Other Aliphatic Aldehydes,** Anal. Chem. **35,** 733 (1963).

A method is described for the analysis of formaldehyde using an-throne as the color-forming reagent. The method appears to be applicable to air samples containing elevated concentrations of the aldehyde. More work needs to be done to determine sampling solutions, sampling rates and sensitivities before the method can be used routinely.

Hanson, N. W., D. A. Reilly, and H. E. Stagg, Eds. *The Determination of Toxic Substances in Air* (Cambridge, England: W. Heffer and Sons, Ltd., 1965), p 131.

See Also

1. Kersey, R. W., J. R. Maddocks, and T. E. Johnson. Analyst **65,** 203 (1940).
2. Barnes, E. C., and H. W. Speicher. J. Ind. Hyg. Toxicol. **24,** 10 (1942).

Formaldehyde, in concentrations from 2–20 ppm in a 0.5-liter air sample, can be determined by this method. The sample is collected in a midget impinger containing 10 ml phenylhydrazine hydrochloride. The sample is quantitatively transferred to a 25-ml volumetric flask. Potassium ferricyanide and hydrochloric acid are added to the sample, and the optical density of the resulting magenta-stained solution is read in a spectrophotometer at 515 mμ. The quantity of formaldehyde present in the sample is read from a previously prepared calibration curve, and the airborne concentration is calculated.

The sampling rate through the impinger should be approximately 1 lpm.

Interferences

Iron in any form will interfere and other aldehydes will cause some degree of interference.

The method is simple and requires approximately 1.5 hours for completion. No special or expensive equipment is required. The method is suitable for industrial hygiene work, and, if the duration of sampling is long enough, the method should be applicable for air pollution work.

Lyles, G. R., F. B. Dowling, and V. J. Blanchard. **Quantitative Determination of Formaldehyde in the Parts per Hundred Million Concentration Level,** J.A.P.C.A. **15,** 106 (1965).

Formaldehyde, in concentrations above one part per hundred million, can be determined by this method if one cubic foot of air is sampled. The air sample is collected in water in a midget impinger. A solution of sodium sulfite in sodium tetrachloromercurate is added to the sample. An acidic solution of pararosaniline hydrochloride is added to produce a blue-violet color, which is read in a spectrophotometer at 560 mμ.

Sampling Procedure

The sampling rate can be 0.2 cfm through the midget impinger and at least 1 cfm of air should be sampled.

Interferences

Acetaldehyde and propionaldehyde interfere slightly.

The method is relatively specific for formaldehyde in air and can be used in industrial hygiene and air pollution work. Analysis requires somewhat more than 1 hour for completion.

Ekberg, D. R., and E. C. Silva. **Rapid Spectrophotometric Method for Formaldehyde Detection,** Anal. Chem. **38,** 1421 (1966).

Formaldehyde, in concentrations ranging from 1–3 ppm, can be determined by this method. Two ml of the sample solution are quantitatively transferred to a test tube. A sulfuric acid–ferric chloride solution is added followed by the addition of a proteose–peptone solution. The sample is heated in a water bath and then cooled. The absorbance of the resulting violet-colored solution is read in a spectrophotometer at a wavelength of 550 mμ. The quantity of formaldehyde present is read from a calibration curve, and the airborne concentration is calculated.

Sampling Procedure

Collection in a fritted bubbler containing 10 ml of distilled water appears to be a feasible collection method. A sampling rate of 2 lpm should be adequate.

Interferences

Acetaldehyde, butyraldehyde, and diacetone alcohol interfere with the color development.

The method requires approximately 1 hour for complete analysis and is suitable for air pollution work.

Cares, J. W. **Determination of Formaldehyde by the Chromotropic Acid Method in the Presence of Oxides of Nitrogen,** Am. Ind. Hyg. Assoc. J. **29,** 405 (1968).

The interference of nitrogen oxides in the determination of formaldehyde by the chromotropic acid method has been greatly reduced. The sample is collected in sodium bisulfite and then analyzed by the chromotropic acid method.

Albrecht, A. M., W. I. Scher, Jr., and H. J. Vogel. **Determination of Aliphatic Aldehydes by Spectrophotometry,** Anal. Chem. **34,** 398 (1962).

Formaldehyde can be determined quantitatively at concentrations below 0.4 moles per ml of sampling solution. The air sample is collected in a midget impinger containing 10 ml of distilled water. To an aliquot of this sample is added a solution of methylamine hydrochloride in sodium pyrophosphate followed by the addition of a solution of o-aminobenzaldehyde. The absorbance of the yellow-colored reaction mixture is read at 440 mμ in a spectrophotometer. The quantity present is read from a calibration curve.

The sampling rate may be 0.1 cfm through a midget impinger or 1 cfm through a standard impinger. Scrubbers or gas washing bottles may be used. A sampling duration of 30 minutes will usually collect a suitable sample.

Interferences

Other aliphatic aldehydes interfere and many of them can be determined by this method.

The method is useful for atmospheric sampling and analysis and should be adaptable for use at stack concentrations. Analysis requires approximately 1 hour.

Glycolaldehyde

Basson, R. A., and T. A. Du Rlessis. **A Spectrophotometric Method for the Microdetermination of Glycolaldehyde,** Analyst **92,** 463 (1967).

This method was not designed specifically for industrial hygiene use but does appear to be satisfactory for air analysis. Clycolaldehyde is soluble in water and presumably can be collected in a midget fritted bubbler or a large fritted bubbler.

Glycolaldehyde in concentrations ranging from 0.5–5 μg per ml of solution can be determined by this method. An aliquot of solution can be determined. An aliquot of the sample along with a solution of dinitrophenyl is heated in a water bath for 1 hour. After cooling, the sample is quantitatively transferred to a separatory funnel and extracted twice with benzene. Sodium ethoxide solution is added and the sample diluted with ethyl alcohol. The resulting blue color is read in a spectrophotometer at a wavelength of 560 mμ. The quantity of glycolaldehyde present in the sample is read from calibration curve, and the airborne concentration is calculated.

Sampling Procedure

The sample should be collected in a fritted bubbler containing distilled water or a large fritted bubbler containing 100 ml distilled water. Airflow rates of 2–10 lpm should be adequate. The duration of sampling will be determined by the expected concentration of glycolaldehyde. At least 5 μg per ml of sampling solution should be collected.

Interferences

It appears that other similar aldehydes will interfere. This method seems to be suitable for industrial hygiene work.

Guaiazulene

Sawicki, E., T. W. Stanley, and W. C. Elbert. **Spot Test Detection and Spectrophotometric Determination of Azulene Derivatives with 4-Dimethylaminobenzaldehyde,** Anal. Chem. **33,** 1183 (1961).

Guaiazulene can be determined in concentrations as low as one part guaiazulene in five million parts of sample solution. No data were presented on collection methods but it appears that a sample could be collected in ethyl or methyl alcohol. A solution of 4-dimethylaminobenzaldehyde in acetic acid is added to the alcoholic sample. Hydrochloric acid and trichloracetic acid are added and the resulting blue color is allowed to develop for 15 minutes. The absorbance is read in a spectrophotometer at 642 mμ and compared with a standard curve.

No information on sampling rates is given but 1 cfm through a Greenburg-Smith impinger containing 75–100 ml alcohol seems to be reasonable.

Interferences

Other azulene compounds will interfere. Pyrroles and indoles are the other main possible interferences.

The method is sufficiently sensitive to be used for air pollution analysis. Analysis requires about 30 minutes.

Hexafluoropropene

Marcoli, K., and A. L. Linch. **Perfluoroisobutylene and Hexafluoropropene Determination in Air,** Am. Ind. Hyg. Assoc. J. **27,** 360 (1966).

Hexafluoropropene, in concentrations above 0.1 ppm, can be determined by this method. The air sample is collected in two midget impingers connected in series, each containing methyl alcohol. During sample collection the impingers are cooled in a methanol–dry ice bath. The collected sample is reacted with pyridine and piperidine and allowed to stand for 1 hour. The resulting yellow color is read in a spectrophotometer at 412 mμ. The quantity of hexafluoropropene present is determined from a calibration curve, and the airborne concentration is calculated.

Sampling Procedure

A sampling rate below 0.1 cfm is satisfactory for a duration of 10–20 minutes. If a 0.1 cubic foot sample is collected, this analytical method will detect 0.02 ppm. This can be improved by collecting longer samples.

Interferences

Perfluoroisobutylene, tetrafluoroethylene, trifluoroethylene, chlorotrofluorethylene, 1,1-dichlorodifluoroethylene, and carbon tetrachloride interfere with this determination.

Analysis requires 3–4 hours for completion. Preparation of standards is an involved procedure.

Hexaldehyde

Ruch, J. E., and J. B. Johnson. **Determination of Aldehydes by Mercurimetric Oxidation,** Anal. Chem. **28,** 69 (1956).

Hexaldehyde, in the parts per million range, can be determined by this method. This method is not designed for air analysis and a sampling procedure must be devised. The sample is quantitatively transferred to an Erlenmeyer flask, and 50 ml of a solution of potassium iodide in potassium hydroxide are added. The sample is kept cool in an ice bath, and the 50 ml of agar and 25 ml of glacial acetic acid are added. A standardized iodine solution is then added, and after 15 minutes the sample is titrated with standardized thiosulfate solution. The quantity of aldehyde present is then calculated.

Sampling Procedure

No air sampling procedure has yet been developed.

Interferences

Alcohol and esters interfere slightly with this determination. Some vinyl compounds, unsaturated aldehydes, acetone, and methyl ethyl ketone also interfere slightly.

Hexanone

Jacobs, Morris B. *The Analytical Chemistry of Industrial Poisons, Hazards and Solvents,* 2nd ed. (New York: Interscience Publishers, Inc., 1949), p 690.

See Also

Patty, F. A., H. H. Schrenk, and P. Yant.   U.S.P.H.S. Reprint **1702** (1935).

2-Hexanone, in the parts per million range, can be determined by this method. The sample is collected in a flask containing 50 ml of a standardized solution of sodium hydroxide. The flask is equipped with a stopper containing a glass stopcock. The flask is series-connected with a mercury U-tube monometer and partially evacuated. After closing the stopcock, the bottle may be taken to the field and a sample collected by vacuum displacement. The sample volume is then calculated. The ketone is absorbed by the sodium hyd-oxide and an excess of a standardized iodine solution is added. After 15 minutes the sample is neutralized with sulfuric acid and the excess iodine is titrated with a standardized sodium thiosulfate solution. The quantity of methyl ethyl ketone found must be multiplied by 0.103 to allow for the secondary reactions which occur during the analysis. The airborne concentration can then be calculated.

Interferences

Other ketones as well as any material which is reactive with iodine will interfere.

Analysis requires approximately 2 hours to complete. The method is suitable for industrial hygiene but not for air pollution work.

Hexylamine

Scherberger, R. F., F. H. Miller, and D. W. Fasset. **The Determination of N-Butylamine in Air,** Am. Ind. Hyg. Assoc. J. **21,** 471 (1960).

Hexylamine, in concentrations above 0.1 ppm in a one-cubic-foot air sample, can be determined by this method. The air sample is collected in a gas washing bottle or midget fritted impinger containing a solution of concentrated hydrochloric acid and isopropyl alcohol. An aliquot of less than 3 ml is used for analysis. Pyridine and ninhydrin in isopropyl alcohol are added to the sample which is then heated in a water bath for 7 minutes. The sample is next cooled for 10 minutes in a cold water bath. The absorbance of the resulting solution is read in a spectrophotometer at 575 mμ. The concentration of hexylamine in the sample is determined from a calibration curve, and the airborne concentration is calculated.

Sampling Procedure

A sampling rate of 0.1 cfm for periods ranging upwards of 10 minutes is satisfactory for collection of the amine if a fritted midget bubbler is used.

Interferences

The method is not specific for any one amine and other amines will interfere.

Determination is simple and rapid, requiring approximately 2 hours for completion. The method is applicable to industrial hygiene work and in some cases to air pollution analysis.

Hong, W. H., and K. A. Conners. **Spectrophotometric Determination of Aliphatic Amines by Acylation with Cinnamic Anhydride,** Anal. Chem. **40,** 1273 (1968).

n-Hexylamine, in concentrations at the parts per million level, can be determined by this method, which was not designed specifically for air analysis but appears to be applicable. A 1-ml aliquot of the sample is quantitatively transferred to a 50-ml volumetric flask. Cinnamic anhydride solution and tri-*n*-butylamine in acetonitrile are added, mixed and allowed to react at room temperature for several minutes. Sodium hydroxide is added to the 50-ml mark and allowed to stand for 10 minutes. The sample mixture is quantitatively transferred to a separatory funnel and extracted with chloroform. The chloroform extract is washed with distilled water and filtered into a 50-ml volumetric flask. The sample is made to volume with chloroform and the absorbance of the sample is read in a spectrophotometer at 274 mμ. The airborne concentration of *n*-hexylamine is calculated.

Sampling Procedure

An air sampling procedure must be developed. Collection might be accomplished using a fritted bubbler containing an acetonitrile solution.

Interferences

Any aliphatic amine will interfere with this method.

Hashmi, M. H., and A. A. Ayaz. **The Determination of Methyl Ketones and Acetaldehydes by Titration with Hypobromite Using Bordeaux Indicator,** Anal. Chem. **36,** 385 (1964).

Hexanone can be simply, accurately and rapidly determined with this method. The method, although not designed for an air analysis, should be applicable with some modification. The sample could be collected in water using an impinger or a fritted bubbler. A measured aliquot of sample is placed in a flask, 3*N* sodium hydroxide is added, and the mixture is titrated against standard hypobromite solution using Bordeaux as an internal indicator. The end point shows up as a change from light pink to faint yellow or colorless.

A sampling rate of about 1–2 lpm should be adequate for collection of the sample.

Interferences

Aliphatic aldehydes and methyl ketones will interfere, as will high concentrations of aldehydes.

The method should have application in ambient air, industrial hygiene and stack gas analysis. Analysis should require less than 1 hour to complete.

Hexyl Mercaptan

Moore, H., H. L. Helwig, and R. J. Grave. **A Spectrophotometer Method for the Determination of Mercaptans in Air,** Am. Ind. Hyg. J. **21,** 466 (1960).

Hexyl mercaptan, in concentrations above about 0.5 ppm in a 1-liter air sample, can be rapidly and accurately determined by this method. The air sample is collected in a fritted bubbler containing mercuric acetate solution. The sample is placed in a volumetric flask and diluted with distilled water. *N,N*-Dimethyl-*p*-phenylenediamine in hydrochloric acid and ferric chloride in nitric acid solution are added to the sample. The resulting red color is allowed to develop for 30 minutes and read in a spectrophotometer at 500 mμ. Standards are prepared from lead methyl mercaptide.

Sampling Procedure

Sampling rates of less than 0.5 lpm for a fritted bubbler and 1.5 lpm for a large bubbler are satisfactory for collection of the mercaptan. A 30-minute sample is usually sufficient.

Interferences

This method is not specific for any one mercaptan and all mercaptans will interfere. Hydrogen sulfide, sulfur dioxide, and nitrogen dioxide do not interfere at the concentrations usually found in air pollution or industrial hygiene studies.

The method is applicable to both industrial hygiene and air pollution work. It requires about 2 hours for completion.

Hydrazine

Dambrauskas, T., and H. H. Cornish.   **A Modified Spectrophotometric Method for the Determination of Hydrazine,** Am. Ind. Hyg. Assoc. J. **23,** 151 (1962).

Hydrazine, in concentrations above 0.00076 ppm, can be determined by this method. The method as detailed is used for hydrazine in urine but appears to be applicable to air samples if collected in an aqueous solution. The sample containing the hydrazine is reacted with a solution of *p*-dimethylaminobenzaldehyde in methanol and acetic acid. This mixture is allowed to stand for 4 hours and then is diluted to volume with glacial acetic acid. The resulting color is read in a spectrophotometer at 480 mμ.

The method is applicable to industrial hygiene work; about 5 hours are required for completion of the analysis.

Hydrazoic Acid

Hanson, N. W., D. A. Reilly, and H. E. Stagg, Eds.   *The Determination of Toxic Substances in Air* (Cambridge, England: W. Heffer and Sons, Ltd., 1965), p 135.

Hydrazoic acid, in concentrations from 0.3–17 ppm in a 25-liter air sample, can be determined by this method. The air sample is collected in a midget impinger containing a sodium hydroxide solution. The sample is quantitatively transferred to a 50-ml volumetric flask. Potassium nitrate and nitric acid are added to the sample. The sample should then be at pH 7.0; if it is not, the pH is adjusted with either sodium hydroxide or nitric acid. Ferric chloride solution is added and the entire sample is diluted to 50 ml with potassium nitrate. The optical density of the resulting red-colored solution is read in a spectrophotometer at a wavelength of 485 mμ. The quantity of hydrazoic acid present in the sample is determined from a previously prepared calibration curve, and the airborne concentration is calculated.

The sampling rate through the impinger should be approximately 2.5 lpm for at least 10 minutes.

Interferences

This method appears to be relatively specific for hydrazoic acid.

The method is simple and requires approximately 45 minutes for complete analysis. No special or expensive equipment is required and the method is suitable for industrial hygiene work.

Halogenated Hydrocarbons

Campbell, E. E., M. F. Milligan, and H. M. Miller. **Evaluation of Methods for the Determination of Halogenated Hydrocarbons in Air,** Am. Ind. Hyg. Assoc. J. **20,** 138 (1959).

Four methods for the determination of halogenated hydrocarbons are compared. These are the Fujiwara method, the mercuric thiocyanate method, the mercuric nitrate method, and the silver nitrate method.

Hydrogen Chloride

Hanson, N. W., D. A. Reilly, and H. E. Stagg, Eds. *The Determination of Toxic Substances in Air* (Cambridge, England: W. Heffer and Sons, Ltd., 1965), p 138.

Hydrogen chloride, in concentrations above 2.5 ppm in a 100-liter air sample, can be determined by this method. The air sample is collected in a gas washing bottle containing 25 ml distilled water. After collection, the sample is quantitatively transferred to a beaker. Nitric acid is added to the sample, which is then titrated potentiometrically with silver nitrate. The airborne concentration of hydrogen chloride is calculated.

The sampling rate through the gas washing bottle should be about 5 lpm until 100 liters of air have been sampled.

Interferences

Any halide will interfere with this method.

The method is simple and rapid, requiring approximately 45 minutes for complete analysis. No special or expensive equipment is required. This method is suitable for industrial hygiene work, but it is not considered sufficiently sensitive for air pollution work.

Hanson, N. W., D. A. Reilly, and H. E. Stagg, Eds. *The Determination of Toxic Substances in Air* (Cambridge, England: W. Heffer and Sons, Ltd., 1965), p 137.

Hydrogen chloride, in concentrations from 2–16 ppm in a 5-liter air sample, can be determined by this method. The air sample is collected in two midget impingers connected in series. Each impinger contains distilled water. The air sample is quantitatively transferred to a 50-ml Nessler tube. Silver nitrate is added to the sample and allowed to stand in the dark for 5 minutes. The resulting turbidity is compared to a series of standards prepared from sodium chloride. The airborne concentration of hydrogen chloride is then calculated.

The sampling rate through the two impingers should be approximately 0.75 lpm for a period long enough to collect 5 liters of air.

Interferences

Any halide or compound giving up its halide ion easily will interfere with this method.

The method is simple and rapid, requiring approximately 30 minutes for complete analysis. No special or expensive equipment is required and the method is suitable for industrial hygiene work. This method is not considered sensitive enough for air pollution work, although it might be usable with a long sampling time.

Jacobs, Morris B. *The Analytical Toxicology of Industrial Inorganic Poisons* (New York: Interscience Publishers, Inc., 1967), p 729.

See Also
1. Nicholson, R. I.   Analyst **66**, 189 (1941).
2. Epstein, J.   Anal. Chem. **19**, 272 (1947).

Hydrogen chloride, in concentrations from 0.2–1.2 per ml, can be determined by this method. The sample is collected in a fritted bubbler containing water as the collecting medium. One ml of the sample is quantitatively transferred to a test tube and a solution of chloramine-T is added. After 1 minute a solution of 3-methyl-1-phenyl-5-pyrazolone in pyridine is added to the sample. After 20 minutes the optical density of the resulting solution is read in a spectrophotometer at a wavelength of 630 mμ. The quantity of cyanide present in the aliquot analyzed is read from a calibration curve prepared from sodium cyanide, and the airborne concentration is calculated.

Sampling Procedure

The sample can be collected in a fritted bubbler at a rate of 2–3 lpm for 30 minutes.

Interferences

The method appears to be relatively specific for cyanide ions including hydrogen cyanide.

This method is suitable for industrial hygiene work but would require a very long sampling time to be considered useful for air pollution work. Preparation of the pyrazolone reagent requires approximately 5 hours while the rest of the analysis can be completed in 1 hour.

Hydrogen Cyanide

Robbie, W. A., and P. J. Leinfelder.   **A Rapid and Simple Method for Measuring Small Amounts of Cyanide Gas in Air,** J. Ind. Hyg. Toxicol. **20**, 136 (1945).

Hydrogen cyanide, in concentrations greater than 1 part in 50 million, can be determined by this method if a 10-liter air sample is used. The air sample is scrubbed through a fritted bubbler containing a phosphate buffer and phenolphthalein reagent. A 0.1% potassium hydroxide solution is added to the sample and the resulting red color is read in a spectrophotometer. The quantity of cyanide in the sample is determined from a calibration curve.

Sampling Procedure

The sampling rate through the fritted bubbler may be maintained at 1 lpm; the sampling time varies from 15–30 minutes depending on the expected concentration.

Interferences

Free halogens, hydrogen sulfide, and phenol will interfere with the determination of hydrogen cyanide.

The method is suitable for both industrial hygiene and ambient air analysis. Stack gas analysis may be conducted when certain modifications in collection are made. The method is rapid, requiring less than 1 hour to complete.

Epstein, J. **Estimation of Microquantities of Cyanide,** Anal. Chem. **19,** 273 (1947).

Hydrogen cyanide in concentrations above 0.2 μg and below 1.2 μg can be determined by this method. The cyanide is reacted with chloramine-T to produce cyanogen chloride, which is reacted with a pyridine–pyrazolone solution. The optical density of the resulting blue color is read in a spectrophotometer and compared with a set of standards.

Hanker, J. B., R. M. Gamson, and Harold Klapper. **Fluorometric Method for Estimation of Cyanide,** Anal. Chem. **29,** 879 (1957).

Hydrogen cyanide, in the parts per million range, can be determined by this method. Chloramine-T is used to convert the hydrogen cyanide to cyanogen chloride. The cyanogen chloride is reacted with nicotinamide producing a solution with a blue fluorescence which is measured and compared with a series of standards prepared from potassium cyanide.

Sampling Procedure

The sample may be collected in two bubblers connected in series at a rate of 0.5 lpm. The sampling duration depends upon the concentration present; approximately 0.3 μg hydrogen cyanide should be collected.

Jacobs, Morris B.   *The Chemical Analysis of Air Pollutants* (New York: Interscience Publishers, Inc., 1960), p 248.

See Also

Hanker, J. S., A. Gelberg, and B. Withen.   Anal. Chem. **30**, 93 (1958).

Cyanide (HCN), in concentrations above approximately 0.02 μg cyanide ion per ml of sample solution, can be determined by this method. The sample is collected in a midget impinger containing distilled water. A 1-ml aliquot of the sample is quantitatively transferred to a test tube and a solution of potassium bis-(5-sulfoxino)-palladium II–standardized sodium hydroxide–glycine–magnesium chloride hexahydrate are added. The intensity of the resulting fluorescence is then measured. The quantity of cyanide (HCN) present in the sample is read from a calibration curve prepared from potassium cyanide, and the airborne concentration is calculated.

Sampling Procedure

The sample is collected in a midget impinger containing distilled water at a rate of 2 lpm.

Interferences

The method is considered to be relatively specific for cyanide ion.

This method requires approximately 30 minutes for complete analysis. It is suitable for industrial hygiene work and, if a large sample is collected, it is applicable to air pollution work.

Jacobs, Morris B.   *The Chemical Analysis of Air Pollutants* (New York: Interscience Publishers, Inc., 1960), p 246.

Cyanide (HCN), in concentrations exceeding approximately 1 ppm, can be determined by this method. The sample is collected in a midget impinger containing 10 ml distilled water. A 1-ml aliquot of the sample is added to 1 ml of standardized sodium hydroxide solution, and a solution of potassium bis-(7-iodo-5-sulfoxino)-palladium is added to the sample along with a ferric chloride solution. The bluish color produced is measured in a colorimeter using a 64 filter. The quantity of cyanide present in the sample is read from a calibration curve prepared from potassium cyanide. The airborne concentration of HCN is calculated.

Sampling Procedure

The sample may be collected in a midget impinger containing 10 ml distilled water at a rate of approximately 2 lpm for 15–30 minutes.

Interferences

The method is considered to be relatively specific for cyanide ion.

This method is relatively simple and requires approximately 30 minutes for complete analysis. It is suitable for both air pollution and industrial hygiene work.

Bark, L. S., and H. G. Higson. **A Review of the Methods Available for the Detection and Determination of Small Amounts of Cyanide,** Analyst **88,** 751 (1963).

A detailed review of the methods available for the quantitative determination of cyanide is presented; 122 references are cited.

Hanson, N. W., D. A. Reilly, and H. E. Stagg, Eds. *The Determination of Toxic Substances in Air* (Cambridge, England: W. Heffer and Sons, Ltd., 1965), p 139.

See Also

1. Aldridge, W. N.   Analyst **69,** 262 (1944).
2. Aldridge, W. N.   Analyst **70,** 474 (1945).

Hydrogen cyanide, in concentrations from 0–20 ppm in a 0.2-liter air sample, can be determined by this method. The air sample is collected in a midget impinger containing sodium hydroxide. The sample is quantitatively transferred to a beaker, and solutions of acetic acid, bromine, and arsenious oxide are added rapidly, one after the other. The sample is diluted to 20 ml, and 5 ml of a *p*-toluidine–pyridine reagent is added. The sample is read on a spectrophotometer at a wavelength of 500 mμ. The quantity of hydrogen cyanide present in the sample is read from a previously prepared calibration curve, and the airborne concentration is calculated.

The sampling rate through the impinger should be approximately 0.5 lpm.

Interferences

Thiocyanate, cyanogen bromide, and cyanogen chloride are the only known interferences with this method. The method is simple, requiring approximately 1.5 hours to complete. No special or expensive equipment is required, and the method is suitable for industrial hygiene and air pollution work.

Geulbault, G. G., and D. N. Kramer.   **Ultrasensitive, Specific Method for Cyanide using *p*-Nitrobenzaldehyde and *o*-Dinitrobenzene,** Anal. Chem. **38,** 834 (1966).

A method for the determination of cyanide ion is presented. Cyanide ion in concentrations above 45 nanograms can be determined. An air sampling method must be developed to trap hydrogen cyanide. One possibility might be collection in a fritted bubbler containing sodium hydroxide. After collection, 1 ml of cyanide solution is reacted with *p*-nitrobenzaldehyde, *o*-dinitrobenzene and sodium hydroxide. The rate of change of absorbance with time is plotted, and the airborne concentration of cyanide is calculated.

Interferences

Thirty anions were tested for interference potential. No interferences were found.

This method requires approximately 1 hour for completion.

Jacobs, Morris B.   *The Analytical Toxicology of Industrial Inorganic Poisons* (New York: Interscience Publishers, Inc., 1967), p 733.
See Also
Cupples, H. L.   Ind. Eng. Chem., Anal. Ed. **5,** 50 (1933).

This is a titrimetric method where the hydrogen cyanide is collected in sodium hydroxide. Potassium iodide solution is added and the sample titrated with silver nitrate.

Sampling Procedure

The sample can be collected in a small fritted bubbler containing 10 ml sodium hydroxide solution. The rate of collection should be 1 lpm depending upon the concentration expected.

Jacobs, Morris B.   *The Analytical Toxicology of Industrial Inorganic Poisons* (New York: Interscience Publishers, Inc., 1967), p 730.

Hydrogen cyanide, in concentrations of 20 μg per ml of sample, can be determined by this method. The air sample is collected in two fritted bubblers connected in series, each containing 10 ml of potassium hydroxide to which a few drops of ferrous sulfate solution has been added. After collection, the sample is quantitatively transferred to a beaker and brought to a boil to facilitate the production of ferrocyanide. The sample is cooled, filtered and acidified. A small quantity of ferric chloride is added. The blue color produced is compared with a set of standard solutions prepared from potassium cyanide.

Sampling Procedure

The sample is collected in two bubblers in series at a rate of 2 lpm. Depending upon the expected concentration, a sample of up to 100 liters of air may be collected.

Interferences

The method is relatively specific for hydrogen cyanide. Cyanogen and probably cyanogen chloride interfere as does any material producing cyanide ion.

The sensitivity of the method leaves something to be desired but it can be used in industrial hygiene work. It is not sufficiently sensitive for air pollution work. This method requires approximately 1 hour for complete analysis.

Jacobs, Morris B. *The Analytical Toxicology of Industrial Inorganic Poisons* (New York: Interscience Publishers, Inc., 1967), p 732.

See Also

Francis, C. K., and W. B. Connell. J. Am. Chem. Soc. **35**, 1624 (1913).

Hydrogen cyanide, in concentrations above 3 μg per volume of sample analyzed, can be determined by this method. The air sample is collected in two fritted bubblers in series, each containing 15 cc of a dilute sodium hydroxide solution. The sample is quantitatively transferred to a suitable volumetric flask (25 cc) and brought to volume. A portion, or all, of the sample is placed in an evaporating dish along with a small volume of ammonium polysulfide solution, stirred and evaporated to dryness. The residue is taken up in a little water and a cadmium nitrate solution is added; the solutions are filtered and placed in a Nessler tube. Sulfuric acid and ferric chloride are added to the sample and the resulting red color is compared with a series of standards prepared from potassium cyanide. The airborne concentration of hydrogen cyanide is calculated.

Sampling Procedure

The sample may be collected in two bubblers in series each containing 15 ml of a dilute sodium hydroxide solution. The sample is collected at a rate of 0.5 lpm for 30 minutes or longer if the expected concentration is small.

Interferences

Any other cyanide or cyanate will interfere with this determination.

The method is suitable for industrial hygiene work. If a sufficiently long sampling time is used, this method can be applied to air pollution analysis. The method requires approximately 1.5 hours for complete analysis.

Hydrogen Fluoride

Marshall, B. S., and R. Wood. **A Simple Field Test for the Determination of Hydrogen Fluoride in Air,** Analyst **93,** 821 (1968).

Hydrogen fluoride, in concentrations above approximately 1 ppm in a 0.5-liter air sample, can be determined by this rapid field method. The air sample is collected in a specially constructed test tube bubbler containing 5 ml of a zirconium oxychloride octahydrate–salochrome cyanine R solution. After collection, the color of the sample is compared with a set of prepared color standards, and the concentration is calculated.

Sampling Procedure

The sample is collected at 100 ml per minute for 5 minutes in a special bubbler constructed from a test tube.

Interferences

Aluminum, sulfate and phosphate interfere with this determination.

Analysis requires approximately 10 minutes to complete. This method can be used as a rapid field method in industrial hygiene work. It is not sufficiently sensitive for air pollution work.

Hydrogen Sulfide

Jacobs, M. B., M. M. Braverman, and S. Hochheiser. **Ultramicrodetermination of Sulfide in Air,** Anal. Chem. **29,** 1349 (1957).

Hydrogen sulfide, in concentrations above one part per billion, can be determined by this method. For concentrations below 20 ppb, the air sample is collected at a rate of 1 cfm in a Greenburg-Smith impinger containing an alkaline cadmium sulfate solution. After collection, a small quantity of N,N-dimethyl-p-phenylenediamine in sulfuric acid and ferric chloride is added to the sample in the impinger. The sample is transferred to a volumetric flask and diluted to 50 ml. After 30 minutes the absorbance of the resulting solution is read in a spectrophotometer at 670 mμ. For concentrations above 20 ppb, a midget impinger is used to collect the sample. A sampling rate of 0.1 cfm for 15 minutes will collect enough sample for analysis. The analytical method is the same for these higher concentrations. The quantity of hydrogen sulfide present in the sample is read from a calibration curve, and the airborne concentration is calculated.

The method is suitable for industrial hygiene and air pollution work and requires approximately 2 hours for complete analysis.

Jacobs, M. B. **Techniques for Measurement of Hydrogen Sulfide and Sulfur Oxides,** Nat. Acad. Sci., Nat. Res. Council, Geophy. Monograph **3,** 24 (1959).

The cadmium sulfide and Methylene Blue methods for the determination of hydrogen sulfide are discussed in detail.

Jacobs, Morris B. *The Analytical Toxicology of Industrial Inorganic Poisons* (New York: Interscience Publishers, Inc., 1967), p 544.

See Also

Moskowitz, S. J., J. Siegal, and W. J. Burkke. N.Y. State Ind. Bull. **19,** 33 (1940).

Hydrogen sulfide, in concentrations above approximately 1 ppm, can be determined if a 30-liter air sample is collected. The sample is collected in three gas washing bubblers connected in series, each containing 100 ml of cadmium chloride in sodium hydroxide solution. The contents of the first two bubblers is quantitatively transferred to an

Erlenmeyer flask, and 25 ml of a standardized iodine solution is added. The excess iodine is titrated with a standardized sodium thiosulfate solution. Starch is used as the indicator. The concentration of hydrogen sulfide in air is calculated.

Sampling Procedure

The air sample may be collected at a rate of 0.5 lpm for at least 1 hour.

Interferences

Any compound reactive with iodine will interfere with this method.

The analysis requires about 1.5 hours to complete and is suitable for industrial hygiene work. This method is not sufficiently sensitive for use in air pollution work.

Jacobs, Morris B. *The Analytical Toxicology of Industrial Inorganic Poisons* (New York: Interscience Publishers, Inc., 1967), p 543.

See Also

1. Gardener, E. D., S. P. Howell, and G. W. Jones. U.S. Bur. Mines Bull. **287** (1927).
2. Wallach, A., and E. P. O'Brien. Proc. Montana Acad. Sci. **10**, 39 (1951).

Hydrogen sulfide, in concentrations above 0.5 ppm in a 30-liter air sample, can be determined by this method. The air sample is collected in two fritted bubblers connected in series. Each of the bubblers contains 10 ml of an ammoniacal cadmium chloride solution. After sampling is completed, any sulfur dioxide present is removed by aeration, and the sample is quantitatively transferred to a stoppered flask. If hydrogen sulfide is present, a yellow precipitate can be observed. This precipitate is dissolved with concentrated hydrochloric acid and the sample titrated with a standard iodine solution.

Sampling Procedure

A sampling rate of 2 lpm for 15 minutes through the two bubblers containing 10 ml of cadmium chloride should collect a sample suitable for analysis.

Interferences

Any material reactive with iodine will interfere with this method.

Analysis requires 2 hours to complete. This method is suitable for industrial hygiene work but is not sufficiently sensitive for air pollution work.

Jacobs, Morris B. *The Analytical Toxicology of Industrial Inorganic Poisons* (New York: Interscience Publishers, Inc., 1967), p 545.

See Also

1. Almy, L. H. J. Am. Chem. Soc. **47**, 138 (1925).
2. Sheppard, S. E., and J. H. Hudson. Ind. Eng. Chem., Anal. Ed. **3**, 73 (1930).
3. Budd, M. S., and H. H. Bewick. Anal. Chem. **24**, 1536 (1967).

Hydrogen sulfide concentrations in the parts per million range can be determined by this method. The air sample is collected in a Greenburg-Smith impinger containing 50 ml of a solution of cadmium sulfate in dilute sodium hydroxide. The sample is quantitatively transferred to a 50-ml volumetric flask and a solution of *N,N*-dimethyl-*p*-phenylenediamine in sulfuric acid is added. A small quantity of ferric chloride is added and the sample is allowed to stand for 30 minutes. The optical density of the sample is read from a calibration curve prepared from either sodium sulfide or allylthiourea. The airborne concentration is calculated.

The air sample may be collected in a Greenburg-Smith impinger at a rate of 1 cfm for at least 30 minutes.

Interferences

Other sulfides may interfere with this determination.

Analysis requires approximately 2 hours to complete and is suitable for both industrial hygiene and air pollution work.

Jacobs, Morris B. *The Analytical Toxicology of Industrial Inorganic Poisons* (New York: Interscience Publishers, Inc., 1967), p 564.

In order to analyze for hydrogen sulfide in the presence of carbon disulfide, the air sample is collected in a series of five bubblers or gas washing bottles. The first three bubblers contain 100 ml cadmium chloride in dilute sodium hydroxide solution and are used to collect the hydrogen sulfide. The bubblers are charged with 100 ml alcoholic potassium hydroxide solution and will collect the carbon disulfide. The concentration of hydrogen sulfide can be determined iodometrically. The carbon disulfide can be determined by one of the methods abstracted elsewhere in this volume.

Jacobs, Morris B. *The Analytical Toxicology of Industrial Inorganic Poisons* (New York: Interscience Publishers, Inc., 1967), p 566.

In order to analyze for hydrogen sulfide vapors in the presence of methyl mercaptan and carbon disulfide the air sample is collected in two gas washing bottles containing sodium hydroxide followed by two fritted bubblers containing sodium hydroxide in ethanol. These bubblers are all connected in series. The contents of the gas washing bottles are combined and acidified with hydrochloric acid. Air is drawn through the sampling solution and led through two tubes, one containing calcium chloride, the other containing finely divided lead acetate. This second tube is connected to a small flask which contains a solution of isatin in sulfuric acid. Air is drawn through this entire system for approximately 30 minutes. The hydrogen sulfide can be determined from the color produced in the lead acetate, while the methyl mercaptan can be spectrophotometrically determined from the depth of the green color produced in the isatin–sulfuric acid solution.

The contents of the two fritted bubblers are combined and acidified with acetic acid and a solution of cupric acetate is added. The solution is allowed to stand for 2 hours, and the yellow copper xanthate is then filtered off. The concentration of carbon disulfide is determined from the quantity of copper present. The copper concentration is determined iodometrically.

This method requires 3–4 hours for complete analysis and can be used in industrial hygiene work.

Iodine

Johannesson, J. K. **Determination of Microgram Quantities of Free Iodine Using o-Tolidine Reagent,** Anal. Chem. **28,** 1475 (1956).

Iodine, in concentrations greater than 0.05 ppm, can be determined by this method if a 10-liter air sample is collected. The sample is collected in a midget impinger or fritted bubbler containing 10 ml o-tolidine–mercuric chloride reagent. During collection the iodine produces a yellow color in the solution. The yellow color is compared with a set of color standards prepared from potassium dichromate, and the airborne concentration is calculated.

Sampling Procedure

The air sample is collected in a midget impinger or fritted bubbler containing 10 ml o-tolidine–mercuric chloride reagent, at a rate of 2 lpm. The sampling time should be no longer than 5 minutes.

Interferences

Among the known interfering materials are iron, manganese, nitrite, and free chlorine.

The method is suitable as a field method in industrial hygiene; analysis requires approximately 30 minutes to complete.

Iodoform

Jacobs, M. B. *The Analytical Chemistry of Industrial Poisons, Hazards and Solvents*, 2nd ed. (New York: Interscience Publishers, Inc., 1949), p 565.

See Also

1. Cole, W. H.   J. Biol. Chem. **71**, 173 (1926).
2. Gettler, A. O., and H. Blume. Arch. Pathol. **11**, 555 (1931).
3. Ross, J. H.   J. Biol. Chem. **58**, 641 (1923/24).

Iodoform in the parts per million range can be determined by this method. The air sample is collected in a bubbler containing 95% ethyl alcohol. After collection, the sample is quantitatively transferred to a volumetric flask and diluted to volume. Pyridine, sodium hydroxide, and an aliquot of the sample are placed in a test tube and heated in a water bath for 1 minute. The resulting color in the pyridine layer is compared with a set of color standards in a color comparator. The permanent color standards are prepared from basic Fuchsin in acidified ethyl alcohol. The concentration of iodoform in air is calculated.

Sampling Procedure

The air sample is collected in a bubbler containing either dilute hydrochloric acid or ethyl alcohol. A sampling rate of 2 lpm for at least 30 minutes should provide an adequate sample.

Interferences

Any material with a 3 halogen-carbon linkage will interfere with this determination. Examples of such compounds are bromoform, iodoform, Chloretone and chloral.

Analysis requires approximately 1 hour to complete. This method is applicable to industrial hygiene work but is not sufficiently sensitive for air pollution analysis.

Iron Pentacarbonyl

Brief, R. S., R. S. Ajemian, and R. G. Confer. **Iron Pentacarbonyl: Its Toxicity, Detection and Potential for Formation,** Am. Ind. Hyg. Assoc. J. **28,** 21 (1967).

Iron pentacarbonyl, in concentrations above 0.009 ppm, can be determined by this method if a 50-liter air sample is collected. The air sample is collected in a midget impinger containing a solution of hydrochloric acid, iodine and potassium iodide. The sample is first decolorized with sodium sulfide, which removes excess iodine. The iron in the sample is reduced to ferrous ion with hydroxylamine hydrochloride. The sample is next buffered at pH 5.0 with sodium acetate, and 1,10-phenanthroline is added to develop the orange-red color in the presence of iron pentacarbonyl. The color is read in a spectrophotometer at a wavelength of 508 mμ. The color is stable and proportional to the concentration of iron present. Standards may be prepared from pure iron wire.

Sampling Procedure

A sampling rate of approximately 3 lpm is satisfactory for sample collection. The sampling duration should be long enough to collect approximately 50 liters of air.

Interferences

Chromium, copper, nickel, cobalt, zinc, cadmium, and mercury interfere with this method but the interference can be removed by an extraction procedure using isopropyl alcohol.

The method is simple and requires approximately 1–1.5 hours to complete. This determination is applicable to industrial hygiene work and is sensitive enough for use in air pollution work in those rare instances when this compound is found in the atmosphere.

Isoamyl Acetate

Hanson, N. W., D. A. Reilly, and H. E. Stagg, Eds. *The Determination of Toxic Substances in Air* (Cambridge, England: W. Heffer and Sons, Ltd., 1965), p 37.

See Also

Hestrin, S. J.   J. Biol. Chem. **180**, 249 (1949).

Isoamyl acetate, in concentrations from 10–400 ppm, can be determined quickly and accurately by this method. The sample is collected in an impinger containing ethyl alcohol. It is quantitatively transferred to a volumetric flask and a solution of hydroxylammonium chloride is added. Following this, sodium hydroxide, hydrochloric acid, and ferric chloride are added to the sample. The sample is then diluted to 25 ml with water and allowed to stand for 30 minutes. The optical density of the resulting purple solution is read in a spectrophotometer at 510 mμ.

Sampling Procedure

The sampling rate should be approximately 0.5 lpm, approximately 0.6 liters of air should be sampled to provide the sensitivity stated above. Increasing or decreasing the volume of air sampled will increase or decrease the concentration range to which this method is applicable.

Interferences

Methyl, butyl and ethyl acetates will interfere with this analysis. The anhydrides and chlorides of carboxylic acids also interfere with this determination.

The method is simple, requiring approximately 1.5 hours to complete and no special or expensive equipment. It is suitable for industrial hygiene work but is not sufficiently sensitive for air pollution work.

Isobutyl Alcohol

Hoare, D. E., and R. R. Ogilvie.   **Spectrophotometric Method for the Microdetermination of Monohydric Aliphatic Alcohols,** Anal. Chem. **38**, 1799 (1966).

This method was not designed for air analysis but appears to be applicable. Isobutyl alcohol in concentrations exceeding 0.1 μg per ml can be determined by this method. The sample may be collected in a midget impinger containing water. An 8-ml aliquot of the sample along with an acetate buffer and sodium nitrite solution are quantitatively transferred to a 50-ml flask.

The sample is incubated at 18°C for 30 minutes, after which heptane is added and it is again incubated at 18°C and agitated. The sample is cooled to 0°C and transferred to a cold separatory funnel; the aqueous layer is removed. The heptane layer is transferred to a test tube and exposed to calcium chloride to remove water. The sample is reacted with α-naphthylamine and incubated at 18°C for 10 minutes. The color is allowed to develop while the sample is contained in a water bath at 60°C for 30 minutes. After cooling, the absorbance of the resulting solution is read in a spectrophotometer at 550 mμ. The concentration present in the sample is read from a calibration curve, and the airborne concentration is calculated.

Sampling Procedure

The sample may be collected by a fritted bubbler at a rate of 2 lpm. Water may be used as the sampling solution.

Interferences

The method is not specific for monohydric aliphatic alcohols but determines many of them.

This method requires approximately 3 hours for complete analysis and is suitable for industrial hygiene work.

Isobutyl Mercaptans

Turk, E., and E. E. Reid. **Copper Alkyl Phthalates for the Estimation of Mercaptans,** Ind. Eng. Chem., Anal. Ed. **17,** 713 (1945).

Isobutyl mercaptans, in concentrations above 40 mg per sample, can be determined by this method. Although the method needs to be tested for air analysis, it appears to have application in certain areas of air pollution work. The sample might be collected in an alcohol solvent using a standard impinger. After collection, the sample is titrated with copper butyl phthalate to a persistent blue-green end point.

A sampling rate of up to 1 cfm through the standard impinger containing 75–100 ml alcohol should be satisfactory.

Interferences

Hydrogen sulfide interferes with the determination; if this gas is present, the method cannot be used. The method determines total mercaptans.

The method could be adapted for stack gas analysis but does not appear to be sufficiently sensitive for air pollution or industrial hygiene work. Analysis requires less than 1 hour for completion.

Isobutyraldehyde

Ruch, J. E., and J. B. Johnson. **Determination of Aldehydes by Mercurimetric Oxidation,** Anal. Chem. **28,** 69 (1956).

Isobutyraldehyde, in the parts per million range, can be determined by this method. It is not designed for air analysis and a sampling procedure must be devised. The sample is quantitatively transferred to an Erlenmeyer flask and 50 ml of a solution of potassium iodide in potassium hydroxide are added to the sample, which is kept cool in an ice bath. Then 50 ml of agar and 25 ml of glacial acetic acid are added. A standardized iodine solution is added; after 15 minutes the sample is titrated with standardized thiosulfate solution. The quantity of aldehyde present is then calculated.

Sampling Procedure

No air sampling procedure has yet been developed.

Interferences

Alcohol and esters interfere slightly with this determination. Some vinyl compounds, unsaturated aldehydes, acetone, and methyl ethyl ketone also interfere slightly.

Isophorone

Kacy, H. W., Jr., and R. W. Cope. **Determination of Small Quantities of Isophorone in Air,** Am. Ind. Hyg. Assoc. Quart. **16,** 55 (1955).

Isophorone, at concentrations above 1 ppm, can be determined by this method. The air is collected in a midget fritted-glass bubbler containing glacial acetic acid. An aliquot of the sample, diluted to 10 cc with acetic acid, is used for analysis. Phosphomolybdic acid in glacial acetic acid is added to the aliquot of the sample and the mixture is heated in a boiling water bath. After cooling, the reaction mixture is again diluted with glacial acetic acid and the absorbance of the resulting blue-colored solution is read in a spectrophotometer at either

650 mμ or 870 mμ. The quantity of isophorone present in the aliquot is determined from a calibration curve and the concentration calculated.

Sampling Procedure

A sampling rate of 1 lpm through the fritted bubbler will produce an efficiency of approximately 85%. Two bubblers in series will increase the efficiency substantially.

Interferences

The method is specific for isophorone in the presence of methyl ethyl ketone, methyl isobutyl ketone, and acetone. These solvents are often used in conjunction with isophorone.

The method is applicable to industrial hygiene analysis and requires approximately 2 hours for completion. It is not sufficiently sensitive for air pollution analysis.

Isopropyl Alcohol

Mantel, M., and M. Anbar.   **Determination of Microgram Amounts of Isopropyl Alcohol in Aqueous Solutions,** Anal. Chem. **36,** 937 (1964).

Isopropyl alcohol, in concentrations from 1.5–30 μg per ml of solution, can be determined by this procedure. The sample can be collected in distilled water using a midget impinger. Ten ml of sample are quantitatively transferred to a separatory funnel. Lithium sulfate, vanadium oxinate reagent, and sodium hydroxide are added to the sample. The resulting pink-colored mixture is centrifuged and the absorbance is read at a wavelength of 380 mμ in a spectrophotometer.

Sampling Procedure

The sampling rate through the midget impinger may be 0.1 cfm. A sampling duration of 30 minutes will usually collect sufficient material for analysis.

Interferences

No discussion of possible interferences is provided although it appears that other alcohols may interfere.

The method appears to be adequate for air analysis and other applications where high sensitivities are required.

Hoare, D. E., and R. R. Ogilvie. **Spectrophotometric Method for the Microdetermination of Monohydric Aliphatic Alcohols,** Anal. Chem. **38,** 1799 (1966).

This method was not designed for air analysis but appears to be applicable for this use. Isopropyl alcohol, in concentrations exceeding 0.1 μg per ml, can be determined by this method. The sample is collected in a midget impinger containing water. An 8-ml aliquot of the sample along with an acetate buffer and sodium nitrite solution are quantitatively transferred to a 50-ml flask.

The sample is incubated at 18°C for 30 minutes, after which heptane is added. The sample is again incubated at 18°C and agitated. The sample is cooled to 0°C and transferred to a cold separatory funnel and the aqueous layer removed. The heptane layer is transferred to a test tube and exposed to calcium chloride to remove water. The sample is reacted with α-naphthylamine and incubated at 18°C for 10 minutes. The color is allowed to develop while the sample is contained in a water bath at 60°C for 30 minutes. After cooling, the absorbance of the resulting solution is read in a spectrophotometer at 550 mμ. The concentration present in the sample is read from a calibration curve and the airborne concentration calculated.

Sampling Procedure

The sample is collected by a fritted bubbler at a rate of 2 lpm. Water may be used as the sampling solution.

Interferences

The method is not specific for monohydric aliphatic alcohols but determines many of them.

The method requires approximately 3 hours for completion and is suitable for industrial hygiene work.

Isobutyl Methyl Ketone

Jacobs, Morris B. *The Analytical Chemistry of Industrial Poisons, Hazards and Solvents,* 2nd ed. (New York: Interscience Publishers, Inc., 1949), p 691.

See Also

Patty, F. A., H. H. Schrenk, and P. Yant. U.S.P.H.S. Reprint #**1702** (1935).

Isobutyl methyl ketone, in the parts per million range, can be determined by this method. The sample is collected in a flask containing 50 ml of a standardized solution of sodium hydroxide and equipped with a stopper containing a glass stopcock. The flask is series-connected with a mercury U-tube monometer and partially evacuated. After closing the stopcock, the bottle may be taken to the field and a sample collected by vacuum displacement. The sample volume is then calculated. The ketone is absorbed by the sodium hydroxide and an excess of a standardized iodine solution is added. After 15 minutes the sample is neutralized with sulfuric acid and the excess iodine is titrated with a standardized sodium thiosulfate solution. The quantity of methyl ethyl ketone found must be multiplied by 0.962 to allow for the secondary reactions which occur during analysis. The airborne concentration can then be calculated.

Interferences

Other ketones as well as any material which is reactive with iodine will interfere.

The method requires approximately 2 hours for complete analysis. It is suitable for industrial hygiene but is not suitable for air pollution work.

Ketene

Deggle, W. M., and J. C. Gage. **The Determination of Ketene and Acetic Anhydride in the Atmosphere,** Analyst **78,** 473 (1953).

A method is described for the determination of ketene in air or in the presence of acetic anhydride in air. The method can determine ketene at a concentration below 1 ppm. The sample is collected in an alkaline hydroxylamine solution. It is reacted with ferric chloride, and the optical density of the resulting solution read in a spectrophotometer at a wavelength of 540 mμ.

Hanson, N. W., D. A. Reilly, and H. E. Stagg, Eds. *The Determination of Toxic Substances in Air* (Cambridge, England: W. Heffer and Sons, Ltd., 1965), p 152.

See Also

Hestrin, S. J.   J. Biol. Chem. **180,** 249 (1949).

Ketene, in concentrations from 0.25–1.5 ppm in an air sample of 200 liters, can be determined by this method. The air sample may be collected in a gas washing bottle containing hydroxyammonium chloride and sodium chloride. After collecting the sample, a solution of ferric chloride is added. The optical density of the resulting purple-colored solution is read in a spectrophotometer at a wavelength of 510 mμ. The quantity of ketene present in the sample is determined from a calibration curve prepared from ethyl acetate. The concentration of ketene in air is calculated.

Sampling Procedure

The sampling rate through the gas washing bottle may be up to 10 lpm for a period sufficient to collect at least 200 liters of air.

Interferences

Any material containing an RCO group will interfere with this determination. Among such materials are esters, acid chlorides, and acid anhydrides.

The method is simple and requires approximately 1.5 hours to complete. No special or expensive equipment is required and the method is suitable for industrial hygiene work as well as air pollution analysis.

Hanson, N. W., D. A. Reilly, and H. E. Stagg, Eds. *The Determination of Toxic Substances in Air* (Cambridge, England: W. Heffer and Sons, Ltd., 1965), p 154.

A method is presented for the determination of ketene in the presence of acetic anhydride. The acetic anhydride is removed, to a large degree, in a prescrubber containing toluene which does not absorb styrene.

Lauryl Mercaptan

Turk, E., and E. E. Reid. **Copper Alkyl Phthalates for the Estimation of Mercaptans,** Ind. Eng. Chem., Anal. Ed. **17,** 713 (1945).

Lauryl mercaptans, in concentrations above 40 mg per sample, can be determined by this method. Although the method needs to be tested for air analysis, it appears to have application in certain areas of air pollution work. The sample might be collected in an alcohol solvent using a standard impinger. After collection, the sample is titrated with copper butyl phthalate to a persistent blue-green end point.

A sampling rate of up to 1 cfm through the standard impinger containing 75–100 ml alcohol should be satisfactory.

Interferences

Hydrogen sulfide interferes with the determination; if this gas is present the method cannot be used. The method determines total mercaptans.

This method could be adapted for stack gas analysis but does not appear to be sensitive enough for air pollution or industrial hygiene work. Analysis requires less than 1 hour for completion.

Malonaldehyde

Kwan, T. W., and B. M. Watts. **A New Color Reaction of Anthrone with Malonaldehyde and Other Aliphatic Aldehydes,** Anal. Chem. **35,** 733 (1963).

A method is described for the analysis of malonaldehyde using anthrone as the color-forming reagent. The method appears to be applicable to air samples containing elevated concentrations of the aldehyde. More work needs to be done to determine sampling solutions, sampling rates, and sensitivities before the method can be used routinely.

Mercaptans

Turk, E., and E. E. Reid. **Copper Alkyl Phthalates for the Estimation of Mercaptans,** Ind. Eng. Chem., Anal. Ed. **17,** 713 (1945).

Mercaptans, in concentrations above 40 mg per sample, can be determined by this method. Although the method needs to be tested for air analysis, it appears to have application in certain areas of air pollution work. The sample might be collected in an alcohol solvent using a standard impinger. After collection, the sample is titrated with copper butyl phthalate to a persistent blue-green end point.

A sampling rate of up to 1 cfm through the standard impinger containing 75–100 ml alcohol should be satisfactory.

Interferences

Hydrogen sulfide interferes with the determination; if this gas is present the method cannot be used. The method determines total mercaptans.

The method could be adapted for stack gas analysis but does not appear to be sensitive enough for air pollution or industrial hygiene work. Analysis requires less than 1 hour for completion.

Methyl Acetate

Goddu, R. F., N. F. Le Blanc, and C. M. Wright. **Spectrophotometric Determination of Esters and Anhydrides by Hydroxamic Acid Reaction,** Anal. Chem. **27,** 1251 (1955).

See Also

Hill, V. T. Ind. Eng. Chem., Anal. Ed. **18,** 317 (1946).

Methyl acetate, in concentrations above 200 ppm in a 25-liter air sample, can be determined by this method. The sample is collected in two fritted bubblers connected in series, each containing ethyl alcohol. It is then reacted with an alkaline hydroxylamine solution. The addition of ferric ion to this mixture produces a highly colored product. The absorbance of this product is read at a wavelength of 530 mμ, and the quantity of ester present is read from a calibration curve. The airborne concentration is calculated.

Sampling Procedure

The air sample may be collected in two fritted bubblers connected in series, each containing 10 ml ethyl alcohol. The sampling rate should be approximately 1–2 lpm until at least 25 liters of air have been sampled.

Interferences

Any other esters, anhydrides, aldehydes, and isocyanates will interfere with this determination.

Analysis requires approximately 2 hours to complete. This method is applicable to industrial hygiene work but is not sufficiently sensitive for air pollution work.

Hanson, N. W., D. A. Reilly, and H. E. Stagg, Eds. *The Determination of Toxic Substances in Air* (Cambridge, England: W. Heffer and Sons, Ltd., 1965), p 37.

See Also

Hestrin, S. J.   J. Biol. Chem. **180**, 249 (1949).

Methyl acetate, in concentrations from 10–400 ppm, can be determined quickly and accurately by this method. The sample is collected in an impinger containing ethyl alcohol. It is quantitatively transferred to a volumetric flask and a solution of hydroxylammonium chloride is added. Following this, sodium hydroxide, hydrochloric acid, and ferric chloride are added to the sample. The sample is then diluted to 25 ml with water and allowed to stand for 30 minutes. The optical density of the resulting purple solution is read in a spectrophotometer at 510 mμ.

The sampling rate should be approximately 0.5 lpm, and approximately 0.6 liters of air should be sampled to provide the sensitivity stated above. Increasing or decreasing the volume of air sampled will increase or decrease the concentration range to which this method is applicable.

Interferences

Ethyl, butyl and isoamyl acetates will interfere with this analysis. The anhydrides and chlorides of carboxylic acids also interfere with this determination.

The method is simple, requires approximately 1.5 hours to complete, and requires no special or expensive equipment. It is suitable for industrial hygiene work but is not sufficiently sensitive for air pollution work.

Methyl Alcohol

Jacobs, M. B.   *The Analytical Chemistry of Industrial Poisons, Hazards and Solvents,* 2nd ed. (New York: Interscience Publishers, Inc., 1949), p 616.

See Also
Jephcott, C. M.   Analyst **60**, 588 (1935).

Methyl alcohol, in concentrations above 30 ppm, can be determined by this method. The air sample can be collected in two fritted bubblers connected in series, each containing 10 ml distilled water. After collection, the sample is quantitatively transferred to a flask. Ethyl alcohol, potassium permanganate, phosphoric acid, oxalic acid, sulfuric acid, and Schiff's reagent are added. After 3 hours the color of the sample is compared with standards in a colorimeter. The airborne concentration is then calculated.

Sampling Procedure
The sample is collected in two fritted bubblers containing distilled water at a rate of 1 or 2 lpm for 30 minutes.

Interferences
Ethyl alcohol does not interfere with this determination. Formaldehyde may interfere.

The method requires approximately 5 hours for complete analysis. It is suitable for industrial hygiene work but is not sufficiently sensitive for air pollution work.

Hanson, N. W., and D. A. Reilly, Eds.   *The Determination of Toxic Substances in Air* (Cambridge, England: W. Heffer and Sons, Ltd., 1965), p 164.

Methyl alcohol, in concentrations from 75–750 ppm in a 1-liter air sample, can be determined by this method. The air sample is collected in a midget impinger containing 10 ml distilled water. The sample is quantitatively transferred to a 25-ml volumetric flask. Solutions of ethyl alcohol, potassium permanganate, and phosphoric acid are added to the sample. After 1 hour, hydrogen peroxide is added to the sample. The optical density of the resulting magenta-colored solution is read in a spectrophotometer at a wavelength of 520 mμ. The quantity of methyl alcohol is determined from a previously prepared calibration curve and the airborne concentration is calculated.

Sampling Procedure
The sampling rate through the midget impinger should be approximately 1 lpm. Concentrations lower than 75 ppm can be determined by extending the sampling time.

Interferences

Formaldehyde, some other aldehydes, materials oxidized to formaldehyde, and iron in any form will interfere with this determination. The method is simple and requires approximately 2.5 hours to complete. It is suitable for industrial hygiene work but is not sufficiently sensitive for air pollution.

Jaselskis, B., and J. P. Warrǐner. **Titrimetric Determination of Primary and Secondary Alcohols by Xenon Trioxide Oxidation,** Anal. Chem. **38,** 563 (1966).

Methyl alcohol, in concentrations above 30 μg, can be determined by this method. An aliquot of the sample containing at least 30 μg of alcohol is quantitatively transferred to an Erlenmeyer flask. The sample is diluted to 20 ml and a known quantity of xenon trioxide standard solution is added. After 2 hours, several drops of sulfuric acid and sodium iodide are added to liberate the triiodide ion. The quantity of xenon trioxide used during the oxidation equals the difference between the xenon trioxide before reaction and after reaction with the alcohol. The quantity of alcohol present is determined from a calibration curve and the airborne concentration calculated.

Sampling Procedure

The sample may be collected in a fritted bubbler containing distilled water at a rate of 2.8 lpm for a period sufficient to collect 30 μg.

Interferences

Halides, amines, carboxylic acids, ketones, and aldehydes interfere with this determination.

The method requires approximately 4 hours for complete analysis. It is suitable for industrial hygiene analysis but is probably not sensitive enough for air pollution work.

Methylaminoethanol

F. A. Miller. **Determination of Diethanolamine and 2-Methylaminoethanol in Air,** Am. Ind. Hyg. Assoc. J. **29,** 411 (1968).

2-Methylaminoethanol above 0.04 ppm in a 25-liter air sample and diethanolamine in concentrations above 0.02 ppm in a 25-liter air sample can be determined by this method. An aliquot of the sample no larger than 2 ml is quantitatively transferred to a stoppered tube. Periodic acid is added to convert a portion of the amine to formaldehyde. After 10 minutes potassium arsenite and chromotropic acid are added to the sample. After heating in a boiling water bath for 30 minutes and cooling, the sample is diluted to 20 ml and the absorbance of the resulting solution is read in a spectrophotometer at a wavelength of 750 mμ. Suitable standards are treated in the same manner.

Sampling Procedure

The sample may be collected in a fritted bubbler containing 10 ml distilled water. A sampling rate of 2 lpm for a period sufficient to collect a 25-liter air sample is satisfactory.

Interferences

Formaldehyde will interfere with this determination; 2-diethylaminoethanol does not.

The method is suitable for industrial hygiene work and requires approximately 2 hours to complete.

p-Methylaniline

Hanson, H. W., D. A. Reilly, and H. E. Stagg, Eds. *The Determination of Toxic Substances in Air* (Cambridge, England: W. Heffer and Sons, Ltd., 1965), p 56.

p-Methylaniline, in concentrations above 1 μg per 10 ml of hydrochloric acid sampling solution, can be determined quickly and easily by this method. The sample is collected in a fritted bubbler containing 10 ml of a standardized hydrochloric acid solution. The sample is quantitatively transferred to a volumetric flask. A sodium nitrite solution is added and allowed to stand for 15 minutes at a temperature below 15°C. Sodium sulfamate, sodium acetate, N-sulfatoethyl-m-toluidine, and hydrochloric acid are added. Full color development occurs in 10 minutes. The optical density of the solution is read on a spectrophotometer at a wavelength of 505 mμ. The quantity of p-methylaniline present is determined from a previously prepared calibration curve, and the airborne concentration is calculated.

The sampling rate through the fritted bubbler should be approximately 5 lpm. The duration of sampling depends on the expected concentration of the amine.

Interferences

Many amines and their derivatives interfere with this method.

The method is relatively simple and requires about 2 hours to complete. No special or expensive equipment is required, and the method is suitable for industrial hygiene work.

Methyl Cellosolve

Elkins, H. B., D. B. Storlazzi, and J. W. Hammond. **Determination of Atmospheric Contaminants. Methyl Cellosolve,** J. Ind. Hyg. Toxicol. **24,** 229 (1942).

Methyl Cellosolve, in concentrations above 2–5 ppm, can be determined by this method. The air sampled is collected in two standard impingers in series, each containing 75 ml distilled water. A 10-ml aliquot is used for analysis. Concentrated sulfuric acid and potassium dichromate are added to the sample and the mixture is refluxed for 4 hours. After cooling, potassium iodide is added and the sample is titrated with standard sodium thiosulfate. The concentration of methyl Cellosolve is calculated from the titration data.

Sampling Procedure

The sampling rate through the two impingers should be maintained between 0.5 and 1 cfm, and at least a 30-cubic foot air sample should be collected.

Interferences

Acetone, isopropyl alcohol, and ethyl Cellosolve are known to interfere. Other alcohols may also interfere.

The method requires several hours for completion primarily because of the required 4-hour refluxing period. This analysis is applicable to industrial hygiene work as well as other areas where high concentration of this material might be found.

Methyl Chloride

Jacobs, Morris B. *The Analytical Chemistry of Industrial Poisons, Hazards and Solvents,* 2nd ed. (New York: Interscience Publishers, Inc., 1949), p 562.

See Also

Patty, F. A., H. H. Schrenk, and W. P. Yant.   Ind. Eng. Chem., Anal. Ed. **4**, 259 (1949).

Methyl chloride, in concentrations exceeding 50 ppm of air can be determined by this method. The air sample is collected by mercury displacement and then introduced into a special combustion apparatus. The chloride produced by this procedure is collected. The sample is titrated with a standardized silver nitrate solution and the resulting precipitated silver chloride is removed by filtration. The solution is back titrated with a standardized potassium thiocyanate solution using ferric alum as the indicator. The airborne concentration of methyl chloride is then calculated.

Interferences

The method is not specific for methyl chloride and many halides can be determined by this method.

The determination requires about 3 hours to complete. The method is suitable for industrial hygiene work even though the lower limit of this method is 50 ppm. This method of analysis is not sufficiently sensitive to be used in air pollution analysis.

Gunther, F. A., and R. C. Blinn.   *Analysis of Insecticides and Acaricides* (New York: Interscience Publishers, Inc., 1955), p 485.

See Also

1. Chisholm, R. D., and L. Kablitsky.   Ind. Eng. Chem., Anal. Ed. **16**, 538 (1944).
2. Blinn, R. C., and F. A. Gunther.   Anal. Chem. **21**, 1289 (1949).

Methyl chloride, in concentrations exceeding a few parts per million, can be determined by this method. The air sample is collected in four sand-containing absorption tubes connected in series. The sand is moistened with ethanolamine. The sand containing the methyl chloride sample is washed into a flask with a solution of acetic acid and water. This solution is titrated with a standard silver nitrate solution using sodium eosin as the indicator. The concentration of methyl chloride is then calculated.

Sampling Procedure

The sampling rate for the collection of methyl chloride should be about 0.1 lpm for optimum efficiency; and the sampling duration should be such that approximately 30 mg of methyl chloride are collected.

Interferences

This method is not specific for the determination of methyl chloride because numerous compounds containing halogen atoms will interfere.

The determination is relatively simple and rapid, requiring no special or expensive equipment. The method is suitable for industrial hygiene work as well as for the determination of methyl chloride as an insecticide. The method is not sufficiently sensitive for general air pollution work.

Methyl 2-Cyanoacrylate

McGee, W. A., F. L. Oglesby, R. L. Raleigh, M. D., and D. W. Fassett, M. D. **The Determination of a Sensory Response to Alkyl 2-Cyanoacrylate in Air,** Am. Ind. Hyg. Assoc. J. **29**, 558 (1968).

Methyl 2-cyanoacrylate, in concentrations above approximately 1 ppm, can be determined by this method. The air sample is collected in a side-arm test tube containing a standardized solution of sodium hydroxide. The sample is quantitatively transferred to a volumetric flask. Chromotropic and sulfuric acid are added, and the sample is heated in a water bath for 30 minutes. After cooling, the optical density is read in a spectrophotometer at a wavelength of 580 mμ. A set of standards is treated in the same manner and a calibration curve is prepared.

Interferences

Formaldehyde will interfere with this determination.

The method is suitable for industrial hygiene work and appears sufficiently sensitive for air pollution work if a large air sample is collected. Analysis requires approximately 2 hours to complete.

MDI

Grim, K. E., and A. L. Linch. **Recent Isocyanate-in-Air Analysis Studies,** Am. Ind. Hyg. Assoc. J. **25,** 285 (1964).

MDI, in concentrations above 0.01 ppm, can be quickly determined by this method. The air sample is collected in a mixture of hydrochloric and glacial acetic acid contained in a midget impinger. The impinger contains 15 ml of the absorbing solution. Sodium nitrite, sulfamic acid, sodium carbonate, and N-(1-naphthyl)ethylenediamine dihydrochloride–hydrochloric acid solution are added to the sample. The absorbance of the resulting color is read at 555 mμ after 30 minutes. The concentration of MDI is determined from a calibration curve.

The method is applicable to industrial hygiene work and, in some cases, to air pollution work. Analysis requires approximately 1 hour to complete.

Hanson, N. W., D. A. Reilly, and H. E. Stagg, Eds. *The Determination of Toxic Substances in Air* (Cambridge, England: W. Heffer and Sons, Ltd., 1965), p 118.

MDI (diisocyanatodiarylmethane), in concentrations from 0.01–0.04 ppm in a 5-liter air sample, can be determined by this method. A specially constructed absorber (described in the original reference) containing 3 ml of a solution of sodium acetate in hydrochloric acid is used to collect the air sample. At least 5 liters of air are sampled. After sampling, the absorbing solution is quantitatively transferred to a flask and a solution of stabilized p-nitrodiazobenzene is added. After being shaken and allowed to stand for 5 minutes 1.5 ml of chloroform is added and the resulting solution is shaken. The chloroform is taken off and placed in a test tube and the color produced is matched visually to a set of previously prepared standards. The concentration of MDI in the atmosphere is then calculated.

The sampling rate through the bubbler should be approximately 1 lpm and the duration should be about 5 minutes.

Interferences

TDI will interfere with this method of analysis.

The method is simple and rapid, requiring approximately 30 minutes to complete. It is considered suitable for industrial hygiene and air pollution analysis although a longer sample would probably be required for air pollution work. The sampling method used will provide a collection efficiency of about 76% and this must be considered when calculating concentration.

Reilly, D. A.   **A Field Method for Determining 4,4'-Diisocyanatodiphenylmethane in Air,** Analyst **92,** 513 (1967).

MDI (4,4'-diisocyanatodiphenylmethane), in concentrations exceeding 0.01 ppm, can be determined by this method. The air sample is collected in a specially constructed bubbler containing 3 ml hydrochloric acid. The sample is quantitatively transferred to a separatory funnel and sodium nitrite, sulfamic acid, sodium hydroxide and 3-hydroxy-2-naphthanilide (Brenthol AS) are added. After the sample stands for 1 minute, sulfuric acid and chloroform are added. The resulting pink color is compared to standards prepared from 4,4'-diaminodiphenylmethane and iron or cobalt. The airborne concentration of MDI in air is calculated.

Sampling Procedure

The air sample is drawn through the bubbler at a rate of 1 lpm for 5 minutes.

Interferences

There are no known interferences with this method.

The method is simple and rapid, requiring approximately 20 minutes for complete analysis. It is suitable as a field method for both industrial hygiene and air pollution work.

Methacrolein

Ruch, J. E., and J. B. Johnson.   **Determination of Aldehydes by Mercurimetric Oxidation,** Anal. Chem. **28,** 69 (1956).

Methacrolein, in the parts per million range, can be determined by this method. This method is not designed for air analysis and a sampling procedure must be devised. The sample is quantitatively transferred to an Erlenmeyer flask and 50 ml of a solution of potassium iodide in potassium hydroxide is added. The sample is kept cool in an ice bath, and then 50 ml of agar and 25 ml of glacial acetic acid are added. A standardized iodine solution is then added, and after 15 minutes the sample is titrated with standardized thiosulfate solution. The quantity of aldehyde present is then calculated.

Sampling Procedure

No air sampling procedure has yet been developed.

Interferences

Alcohol and esters interfere slightly with this determination. Some vinyl compounds, unsaturated aldehydes, acetone and methyl ethyl ketone also interfere slightly.

Methyl Ethyl Ketone

Jacobs, Morris B. *The Analytical Chemistry of Industrial Poisons, Hazards and Solvents*, 2nd ed. (New York: Interscience Publishers, Inc., 1949), p 687.

See Also

Patty, F. A., H. H. Schrenk, and P. Yant. U.S.P.H.S. Reprint #1702 (1935).

Methyl ethyl ketone [2-butanone], in the parts per million range, can be determined by this method. The sample is collected in a flask containing 50 ml of a standardized solution of sodium hydroxide. The flask is equipped with a stopper containing a glass stopcock. The flask is series-connected with a mercury U-tube monometer and partially evacuated. After the stopcock is closed, the bottle may be taken to the field and a sample collected by vacuum displacement. The sample volume is then calculated. The ketone is absorbed by the sodium hydroxide, and an excess of a standardized iodine solution is added. After 15 minutes the sample is neutralized with sulfuric acid and the excess iodine is titrated with a standardized sodium thiosulfate solution. The quantity of methyl ethyl ketone found must be multiplied by 0.935 to allow for the secondary reactions which occur during analysis. The airborne concentration can then be calculated.

Interferences

Other ketones as well as any material which is reactive with iodine will interfere.

Analysis requires approximately 2 hours to complete. This method is suitable for industrial hygiene but is not suitable for air pollution work.

Methyl Isopropyl Ketone

Hashmi, M. H., and A. A. Ayaz. **The Determination of Methyl Ketones and Acetaldehydes by Titration with Hypobromite Using Bordeaux Indicator,** Anal. Chem. **36,** 385 (1964).

Methyl isopropyl ketone can be simply, accurately and rapidly determined with this method. The method, although not designed for air analysis, should be applicable with some modification. The sample could perhaps be collected in water using an impinger or a fritted bubbler. A measured aliquot of sample is placed in a flask and $3N$ sodium hydroxide is added. The mixture is titrated against standard hypobromite solution using Bordeaux as an internal indicator. The end point shows up as a change from light pink to faint yellow or colorless.

A sampling rate of about 1–2 lpm should be adequate for collection of the sample.

Interferences

Aliphatic aldehydes and methyl ketones will interfere, as will high concentrations of aldehydes.

The method should have application in ambient air, industrial hygiene, and stack gas analysis. Analysis should require less than 1 hour to complete.

Methyl Methacrylate

Gisclard, J. B., D. B. Robinson, and P. J. Kuczo. **A Rapid Empirical Procedure for the Determination of Acrylonitrile and Acrylic Esters in the Atmosphere,** Am. Ind. Hyg. Assoc. J. **19,** 43 (1958).

Methyl methacrylate, in concentrations above 10 ppm, can be determined by this method. The air sample is collected in a midget impinger equipped with a specially constructed suction device. Any suction device can be used provided a flow rate of 300 ml can be maintained through the impinger. The impinger contains potassium permanganate, sodium hydroxide, and telluric acid. A 200-ml air sample is pulled through the impinger and sampling solution in 20 seconds. The air sample is collected in this same manner until the permanganate changes color from pink to bluish-green. The concentration of solvent is then determined from a calibration curve showing air volume versus parts per million.

Interferences

Any compound containing double-bonded carbon atoms may interfere with this determination.

The method is suitable for industrial hygiene field work but is empirical in nature; judgment must be exercised when basing recommendations on data provided by it. The method requires about 30 minutes for completion.

Methyl Mercaptan

Moore, H., H. L. Helwig, and R. J. Grave. **A Spectrophotometer Method for the Determination of Mercaptans in Air,** Am. Ind. Hyg. J. **21,** 466 (1960).

Methyl mercaptan, in concentrations above 0.5 ppm in a 1-liter air sample, can be rapidly and accurately determined by this method. The air sample is collected in a fritted bubbler containing mercuric acetate solution. The sample is placed in a volumetric flask and diluted with distilled water. N,N-Dimethyl-p-phenylenediamine in hydrochloric acid and ferric chloride in nitric acid solution are added to the sample. The resulting red color is allowed to develop for 30 minutes and read in a spectrophotometer at 500 mμ. Standards are prepared from lead methyl mercaptide.

Sampling Procedure

Sampling rates of less than 0.5 lpm for a fritted bubbler and 1.5 lpm for a large bubbler are satisfactory for collection of the mercaptan. A 30-minute sample is usually sufficient.

Interferences

The method is not specific for any one mercaptan and all mercaptans will interfere. Hydrogen sulfide, sulfur dioxide, and nitrogen dioxide do not interfere at the concentrations usually found in air pollution or industrial hygiene studies.

This method is applicable to both industrial hygiene and air pollution work. Analysis requires about 2 hours for completion.

Jacobs, Morris B. *The Analytical Toxicology of Industrial Inorganic Poisons* (New York: Interscience Publishers, Inc., 1967), p 566.

To analyze for methyl mercaptan vapors in the presence of hydrogen sulfide and carbon disulfide, the air sample is collected in two gas washing bottles containing a solution of sodium hydroxide followed by two fritted bubblers containing sodium hydroxide in ethanol. These bubblers are all connected in series. The contents of the gas washing bottles are combined and acidified with hydrochloric acid. Air is drawn through the sampling solution and led through two tubes, one containing calcium chloride, the other containing finely divided lead acetate. This second tube is connected to a small flask which contains a solution of isatin in sulfuric acid. Air is drawn through the entire system for approximately 30 minutes. The hydrogen sulfide can be determined from the color produced in the lead acetate while the methyl mercaptan can be spectrophotometrically determined from the depth of the green color produced in the isatin–sulfuric acid solution.

The contents of the two fritted bubblers are combined and acidified with acetic acid, and a solution of cupric acetate is added. The solution is allowed to stand for 2 hours, after which the yellow copper xanthate is filtered off. The concentration of carbon disulfide is determined from the quantity of copper present. The copper concentration is determined iodometrically.

The method requires 3–4 hours for complete analysis and can be used in industrial hygiene work.

Methyl Sulfate

Jacobs, M. B. *The Analytical Chemistry of Industrial Poisons, Hazards and Solvents*, 2nd ed. (New York: Interscience Publishers, Inc., 1949), p 666.

Methyl sulfate, in the parts per million range, can be determined by this method. The air sample can be collected in a sodium hydroxide solution. The quantity of hydrolyzed sulfate present is then determined by the barium sulfate procedure.

Interferences

Sulfate will interfere with this determination.

Methyl Thioglycolate

Turk, E., and E. E. Reid. **Copper Alkyl Phthalates for the Estimation of Mercaptans,** Ind. Eng. Chem., Anal. Ed. **17,** 713 (1945).

Methyl thioglycolate, in concentrations above 40 mg per sample, can be determined by this method. Although the method needs to be tested for air analysis, it appears to have application in certain areas of air pollution work. The sample might be collected in an alcohol solvent using a standard impinger. After collection, the sample is titrated with copper butyl phthalate to a persistent blue-green end point.

A sampling rate of up to 1 cfm through the standard impinger containing 75–100 ml alcohol should be satisfactory.

Interferences

Hydrogen sulfide interferes with the determination; if this gas is present the method cannot be used. The method determines total mercaptans.

This method could be adapted for stack gas analysis but does not appear to be sensitive enough for air pollution or industrial hygiene work. Analysis requires less than 1 hour for completion.

Methyl Vinyl Pyridine

Gisclard, J. B., D. B. Robinson, and P. J. Kuczo. **A Rapid Empirical Procedure for the Determination of Acrylonitrile and Acrylic Esters in the Atmosphere,** Am. Ind. Hyg. Assoc. J. **19,** 43 (1958).

Methyl vinyl pyridine, in concentrations above 10 ppm, can be determined by this method. The air sample is collected in a midget impinger equipped with a specially constructed suction device. Any suction device can be used provided a flow rate of 300 ml can be maintained through the impinger. The impinger contains potassium permanganate, sodium hydroxide, and telluric acid. A 200-ml air sample is pulled through the impinger and sampling solution in 20 seconds. The air sample is collected in this same manner until the permanganate changes color from pink to bluish-green. The concentration of solvent is then determined from a calibration curve showing air volume versus parts per million.

Interferences

Any compound containing double-bonded carbon atoms may interfere with this determination.

The method is suitable for industrial hygiene field work but is empirical in nature; judgment must be exercised when basing recommendations on data provided by this analysis. The method requires about 30 minutes for completion.

Monobromomononitromethane

Jones, L. R., and J. A. Reddick. **Colorimetric Determination of Nitroparaffins,** Anal. Chem. **24,** 1533 (1952).

Monobromomononitromethane, in concentrations above 3 μg in the sample analyzed, can be determined by this method. The sample may be collected in two fritted bubblers containing concentrated sulfuric acid. An aliquot of the sample, up to 10 ml, is quantitatively transferred to a test tube and held in a boiling water bath for 5 minutes. After cooling, resorcinol solution is placed on top of the acid and the sample is mixed slowly. The sample is heated in a water bath and cooled, and the optical density of the resulting red-blue color is read in a spectrophotometer at a wavelength of 560 mμ. The quantity of monobromomononitromethane present is read from a calibration curve and the airborne concentration is calculated.

Sampling Procedure

The sample may be collected in two bubblers, series-connected, containing sulfuric acid. A sampling rate of 2 lpm for a period long enough to collect 5–10 μg will provide an adequate sample.

Interferences

Any aliphatic nitroparaffin will interfere with this determination. Analysis requires approximately 30 minutes to complete. The method is suitable for industrial hygiene work, and if a large enough sample is collected, it is also applicable to air pollution work.

Naphthalene

Jacobs, Morris B. *The Analytical Chemistry of Industrial Poisons, Hazards and Solvents,* 2nd ed. (New York: Interscience Publishers, Inc., 1949), p 550.

Naphthalene can be collected in four bubblers connected in series. The first bubbler is charged with citric acid to remove ammonia, the second and third bubblers are charged with picric acid, while the fourth is used to collect any liquid carried over. A known volume of air is collected at a rate of approximately 2 lpm. After collection, the contents of bubblers two, three and four are combined. The sample is filtered and an aliquot is titrated with a standard sodium hydroxide solution. The airborne concentration of naphthalene is calculated.

Interferences

The method is relatively specific for naphthalene.

Nickel Carbonyl

Brief, R. S., F. S. Venable, and R. S. Ajemion. **Nickel Carbonyl: Its Detection and Potential for Formation,** Am. Ind. Hyg. Assoc. J. 26, 72 (1965).

Nickel carbonyl, in concentrations above 0.001 ppm, can be determined by this method. The air sample is collected in 3% hydrochloric acid solution. A prefilter is used to remove any solid nickel particles so that only the nickel carbonyl is collected. The sample is placed in a separatory funnel and five solutions are added in the following order: phenolphthalein, ammonium hydroxide, sodium hydroxide three drops past the phenolphthalein end point, α-furildioxime in alcohol and water, and finally chloroform. The solution is shaken for 1 minute, and the resulting yellow color developed in the chloroform is read in a spectrophotometer at a wavelength of 435 mμ. The quantity of nickel present is determined from a calibration curve constructed from nickel standards. The concentration of nickel carbonyl is calculated from the volume of air sampled and the weight of nickel in the sample.

Sampling Procedure

The sample is collected in 10 ml dilute hydrochloric acid contained in a midget impinger. The sampling rate is 0.1 cfm and the duration may be 30–60 minutes.

Interferences

Any nickel compound may interfere with this method. Copper may interfere by forming a brown precipitate but this can be removed. Palladium interferes if the solution is acid. Chromium interferes in concentrations above 0.1% while iron and vanadium interfere in concentrations above 0.5%.

The method is quantitative for nickel carbonyl, is simple and rapid, and requires no special or expensive equipment. It is suitable for industrial hygiene and air pollution work. This method requires approximately 1 hour for complete analysis.

Nitrate Esters

Jacobs, Morris B. *The Analytical Chemistry of Industrial Poisons, Hazards and Solvents*, 2nd ed. (New York: Interscience Publishers, Inc., 1949), p 741.

See Also

Yagoda, H., and F. H. Goldman. J. Ind. Hyg. Toxicol. **25**, 440 (1943).

Nitrate esters, in the parts per million range, can be determined by this method. The sample is collected in a midget impinger containing triethylene glycol. After collection, a 5-ml aliquot is quantitatively transferred to a distillation flask, and distilled water, xylenol in triethylene glycol, and sulfuric acid are added. After 10 minutes distilled water is added and the mixture is distilled. The distillate is collected in a small quantity of sodium hydroxide. The yellow color produced is compared with a set of standards prepared from potassium nitrate, and the airborne concentration is calculated.

Sampling Procedure

The sample is collected in a midget impinger containing 10 ml of triethylene glycol at a rate of 3 lpm for 20 minutes.

Interferences

This method is not specific for any nitrate ester but can be used for the determination of any one of them.

The method requires approximately 2 hours for complete analysis. It is suitable for industrial hygiene work but is not sufficiently sensitive for air pollution work.

Nitrite

Selected Methods for the Measurement of Air Pollutants, U.S. Public Health Serv. Publ. #999-AP-11, 64 (1965).

Nitric oxide, in the parts per million range, can be determined by this method. The sample is collected in three small fritted bubblers. The first and third bubblers contain a solution of sulfanilic acid, glacial acetic acid and N-(1-naphthyl)ethylenediamine dihydrochloride, and the second contains an acid permanganate solution. After collection the solution is allowed to stand to fully develop the red-violet color which is read in a spectrophotometer at a wavelength of 550 mμ. The quantity of nitric oxide present in the sample is determined from a calibration curve prepared from sodium nitrite, and the airborne concentration is calculated.

Sampling Procedure

The sample is collected in fritted bubblers at a rate of 0.4 lpm until a definite color is observed in the third bubbler. The first bubbler removes nitrogen dioxide, the second converts nitric oxide to nitrogen dioxide, and the third collects the converted nitrogen dioxide.

Interferences

The interferences caused by ozone, sulfur dioxide, other nitrogen oxides, and other gases found in outdoor air is negligible at the concentrations usually encountered.

The method requires approximately 1.5 hours for complete analysis. It is suitable for both industrial hygiene and air pollution work.

Hartley, A. M., and R. I. Asai. **Spectrophotometric Determination of Nitrate as 4-Nitroso-2,6-Xylenol,** Anal. Chem. **35,** 1214 (1963).

Nitrite, in concentrations from 0–10 ppm, can be determined by this method. Analysis of nitrogen oxides can be carried out by this method provided that the nitrogen oxides are or can be converted to nitrite before analysis.

It appears that the nitrogen oxides could be collected in water or perhaps in the reagent itself, using a fritted bubbler. These solutions should be investigated to determine their collection efficiency. After collection, the solution is reacted with 2,6-xylenol reagent in an acid medium. The absorbance of the sample is read at a wavelength of 306 mμ with a spectrophotometer and the concentration read from a calibration curve.

Interferences

Interferences appear to be negligible.

The method seems suitable for air pollution work. Analysis requires approximately 2 hours for completion.

Sawicki, E., T. W. Stanley, J. Pfaff, and H. Johnson. **Sensitive New Methods for Autocatalytic Spectrophotometric Determination of Nitrite through Free-Radical Chromogens,** Anal. Chem. **35,** 2183 (1963).

Ten methods for the analysis of nitrite ion are described and compared. All the methods appear to be very sensitive and should find application in air pollution, both in ambient air and at stack concentrations. More work needs to be done on sampling procedures before these methods will be of general use.

Foris, A., and T. R. Sweet. **Determination of Small Amounts of Nitrite by Solvent Extraction and Spectrophotometry,** Anal. Chem. **37,** 701 (1965).

Nitrite ion, in concentrations from 0.010–0.40 ppm, can be determined by this method. The method as published is applicable to water analysis but should also be applicable to the determination of nitrogen oxides in the atmosphere. The sample possibly could be collected in a standard impinger or in a gas washing bottle containing 75–100 ml distilled water. A 40-ml neutral aliquot is used for the analysis. 8-Aminoquinoline reagent and 4M sodium acetate are added; the mixture is heated in a constant-temperature water bath at 60°C. After cooling, 10M sodium hydroxide and n-heptanol are added to the sample. The absorbance of the resulting color is read in a spectrophotometer at a wavelength of 465 mμ.

Sampling Procedure

The sampling rate should probably be 0.5–1 cfm.

Interferences

Cupric ion, ferric ion and ammonia all interfere with this method. The determination is simple and should require about 1 hour for completion. The method should be applicable to atmospheric and industrial hygiene analysis.

p-Nitroaniline

Stewart, J. T., T. D. Shaw, and A. B. Ray. **Spectrophotometric Determination of Primary Aromatic Amines with 9-Chloroacridine,** Anal. Chem. **41,** 360 (1969).

The method was not designed for air analysis but appears to be modifiable for this use. Most of these amines have some vapor pressure; therefore, this analysis is abstracted here.

p-Nitroaniline, in concentrations above approximately 10^{-7} moles, can be determined by this method. The sample can probably be collected in ethyl alcohol. After collection, a 1-ml aliquot of the amine is quantitatively transferred to a volumetric flask. A solution of 9-chloroacridine is added and the pH is adjusted to 4.0 with hydrochloric acid. The absorbance of the resulting orange-colored solution is read in a spectrophotometer at 435 mμ.

Sampling Procedure

The sample may be collected in a fritted bubbler at a rate of 2 lpm.

Interferences

Primary amines and acridone will interfere with this determination.

The method requires approximately 1 hour for completion. It is suitable for industrial hygiene work.

Nitrobenzene

Hands, G. C.   **A Field Test for Nitrobenzene Vapour in Air,** Analyst
85, 843 (1960).

Nitrobenzene, in concentration ranging from 0.5–2.0 ppm in a 6-liter
air sample, can be determined by this method. The air sample is collected in a specially constructed bubbler containing 2 ml Cellosolve.
After collection, zinc amalgam and hydrochloric acid are added to the
sample. Five ml of the resulting solution are transferred to a test tube
and sodium carbonate and the sodium salt of 2-naphthol-3,6-disulfonic
acid in sodium carbonate are added to the sample. Ammonia is added
and the resulting color is compared with a series of color standards.
The airborne concentration is calculated.

Sampling Procedure

The sample is collected in specially constructed bubblers containing
2 ml Cellosolve at a rate of 1.5 lpm for 2.5 minutes. This sampling arrangement can be used for the concentration range of .05–2.0 ppm.
The range of the method can be changed by increasing or decreasing
the sample size.

Interferences

Primary amines and aromatic nitro compounds could be expected to
interfere with this method.

The method requires approximately 15 minutes for complete analysis.
The entire determination can be conducted in the field. The method is
suitable for industrial hygiene work and can be used for air pollution
analysis if a long sampling time is used.

Hanson, N. W., D. A. Reilly, and H. E. Stagg, Eds.   *The Determination
of Toxic Substances in Air* (Cambridge, England: W. Heffer and Sons,
Ltd., 1965), p 168.

Nitrobenzene, in concentrations ranging from 0.4–6 ppm in a 12.5-
liter air sample can be determined by this method. The air sample is
collected in a midget impinger containing a slightly alkaline solution
of 2-ethoxyethanol. After collection, the sample is quantitatively transferred to a 25-ml volumetric flask and diluted with distilled water. A
suitable aliquot is placed in a flask equipped with a reflux condenser.
Hydrochloric acid and zinc granules amalgamated with mercury are

added to the sample, which is slowly refluxed. 2-Ethoxyethanol is added, and after cooling the sample is filtered and the filtrate transferred to a 50-ml volumetric flask. Hydrochloric acid, sodium nitrite, sodium carbonate, and 2-naphthol-3,6-disulfonic acid are added. After 10 minutes, ammonium hydroxide is added to the mark. The optical density of the resulting red-colored solution is read in a spectrophotometer at a wavelength of 490 mμ. The quantity of nitrobenzene in the sample is read from a previously prepared calibration curve constructed using aniline. The airborne concentration of nitrobenzene is calculated.

The sampling rate through the impinger should be 1–1.5 lpm for a time long enough to collect at least 12 liters of air.

Interferences

Aniline and materials forming aniline as a reduction product will interfere with this method.

The method is relatively simple and moderately rapid, requiring approximately 2 hours for completion. The method is suitable for industrial hygiene analysis.

Nitroethane

Jacobs, Morris B. *The Analytical Chemistry of Industrial Poisons, Hazards and Solvents,* 2nd ed. (New York: Interscience Publishers, Inc., 1949), p 733.

See Also

Scott, E. W., and J. F. Treon. Ind. Eng. Chem., Anal. Ed. **12,** 189 (1940).

Nitroethane, in concentrations above 1 mg per sample aliquot analyzed, can be determined by this method. The sample may be collected in evacuated flasks containing 0.1N sodium hydroxide and then acidified with a known volume of hydrochloric acid. The final pH of the solution should be 1.25–1.30. Ferric chloride is added, and the resulting pink color is compared with a set of standards in a colorimeter. The airborne concentration is then calculated.

Interferences

Other nitroparaffins will interfere with this analytical method.

The method requires approximately 1.5 hours to complete analysis. The method is suitable for industrial hygiene work but is not sensitive enough for air pollution work.

Cohen, I. R., and A. P. Altshyller. **Spectrophotometric Determination of Primary Nitroparaffins by Coupling with *p*-Diazobenzenesulfonic Acid,** Anal. Chem. **31,** 1638-40 (1959).

Nitroethane, in concentrations ranging to 50 μg per ml, can be determined by this method. The air sample can be collected in 10% methanol using a midget impinger. One ml of the sample solution is used for analysis. To this solution is added a phosphate buffer and *p*-diazobenzenesulfonic acid. The absorbance for nitroethane is read at 395 mμ and the quantity of nitromethane present is determined from a calibration curve. The airborne concentration is calculated.

A sampling rate of 2–4 lpm through the midget impinger containing methanol should be satisfactory for collection. A sampling duration of 30 minutes should collect a sample suitable for analysis.

Interferences

Other primary nitroparaffins and 2-nitro-2-alkyl-1,3-alkanediols interfere with this determination.

The method is quantitative up to 80 μg per ml after which the absorption curve no longer follows Beer's law.

The method requires less than 1 hour to complete and is suitable for industrial hygiene work. It is not sufficiently sensitive for air pollution work.

Nitrogen Dioxide

Altshuller, A. P., and A. F. Wartburg. **Ultraviolet Determination of Nitrogen Dioxide as Nitrite Ion,** Anal. Chem. **32,** 174 (1960).

Nitrogen dioxide, in concentrations ranging from a few hundred to a hundred thousand parts per million, can be determined by this method. The method involves the collection of the sample in sodium or potassium hydroxide followed by ultraviolet absorption analysis at 210 mμ.

Flow rates up to 1–2 lpm can be used for collection of the sample. A sampling time of 30–60 minutes will usually be sufficient.

Interferences

Hypochlorite ion and iodide could interfere with this determination.

The method is not applicable to ambient air analysis but is useful for the analysis of nitrogen dioxide resulting from high temperature combustion sources. The method is relatively rapid and simple, requiring approximately 30 minutes to complete.

Hanson, N. W., D. A. Reilly, and H. E. Stagg, Eds. *The Determination of Toxic Substances in Air* (Cambridge, England: W. Heffer and Sons, Ltd., 1965), p 172.

Nitrogen dioxide, in concentrations from 2–20 ppm in a 2.5-liter air sample, can be determined by this method. The air sample is collected in a 2.5-liter flask which has been evacuated to at least 20 mm mercury. The flask contains a standardized sodium hydroxide solution. After collection, the sample is quantitatively transferred to a 100-ml volumetric flask. A solution of sulfanilic acid in acetic acid (Griess Ilosvay) is added and this is followed by addition of α-naphthylamine in acetic acid solution. After 30 minutes the optical density of the resulting colored solution is read in a spectrophotometer at a wavelength of 530 mμ. The quantity of nitrogen dioxide contained in the sample is read from a previously prepared calibration curve made from sodium nitrite.

Interferences

If nitric oxide is present in the sample, a high result for nitrogen dioxide will be found. The presence of ozone will yield low results for nitrogen dioxide.

The method is simple and requires approximately 1.5 hours for completion. It is suitable for industrial hygiene work but is not sufficiently sensitive for the analysis of nitrogen dioxide as an air pollutant.

Selected Methods for the Measurement of Air Pollutants. U.S. Public Health Serv. Publ. #999-AP-11 (1965).

See Also

Saltzman, B. E. Anal. Chem. **26**, 1949 (1954).

Nitrogen dioxide, in concentrations ranging from a few parts per billion to approximately five parts per million, can be determined by this method. The air sample can be collected in a fritted bubbler containing 10 ml of a solution of sulfanilic acid, glacial acetic acid, and N-(1-naphthyl)ethylenediamine dihydrochloride. After collection, a reddish-violet color develops in the sample. The absorbance of the sample is read in a spectrophotometer at a wavelength of 550 mμ. The quantity of nitrogen dioxide in the sample is read from a calibration curve prepared from sodium nitrite. The airborne concentration is then calculated.

Sampling Procedure

The air sample is collected in a midget impinger containing 10 ml of the absorbing solution at a rate of approximately 0.4 lpm and for a period sufficient to develop a color.

Interferences

The interferences caused by ozone, sulfur dioxide, other nitrogen oxides, and other gases found in outdoor air is negligible at the concentrations usually encountered.

The method requires approximately 1.5 hours to complete the analysis. The method is suitable for both industrial hygiene and air pollution work.

Beatty, R. L., L. B. Berger, and H. H. Schrenk. **Determination of Oxides of Nitrogen by the Phenoldisulfonic Acid Method,** U.S. Bur. Mines, Rept. Invest. **3687** (1943).

The method presented here is similar to those abstracted previously.

Nitrogen Oxides

Cholak, J., and R. R. McNary. **Determination of the Oxides of Nitrogen in Air,** J. Ind. Hyg. Toxicol. **25,** 354 (1943).

Four methods for the determination of nitrogen oxides are detailed. These include the phenoldisulfonic acid method, diphenylamine spot test, titration of liberated iodine, and a polarographic method. Sampling equipment, flow rates and the analytical procedures are detailed.

The methods are not applicable to ambient air sampling work because they are not sufficiently sensitive. These methods should all be applicable to industrial hygiene work and to the analysis of stack gas for nitrogen oxides.

Patty, F. A., and G. M. Petty. **Nitrite Feld Method for the Determination of Oxides of Nitrogen (except N_2O and N_2O_5),** J. Ind. Hyg. Toxicol. **25,** 361 (1943).

Nitrogen oxides in the range of 1–500 ppm can be determined by this method. The air sample is collected in a 50-ml syringe containing 10 ml sulfanilic acid in glacial acetic acid and α-naphthylamine. The resulting color is compared visually with color standards.

Interferences

Inorganic nitrites and ozone will interfere with the determination.

This analytical method is applicable to industrial hygiene analysis but is not sensitive enough for ambient air analysis. The time required for complete preparation of equipment standards and syringe loading is approximately 2 hours.

Saltzman, B. E. **Colorimetric Microdetermination of Nitrogen Dioxide in the Atmosphere**, Anal. Chem. **26**, 1949 (1954).

This method can be used to determine nitrogen oxides at levels in the parts per billion range using a 10-minute sampling duration. The reagent used is N-(1-naphthyl)ethylenediamine dihydrochloride and acetic acid. Samples may be collected in a bubbler containing sulfanilic acid, glacial acetic acid, and N-(1-naphthyl)ethylenediamine. After collection, the absorbance of the resulting red-to-violet color is read in a spectrophotometer at a wavelength of 550 mμ. This method is excellent for air pollution work.

Norwitz, G. **A Colorimetric Method for the Determination of Oxides of Nitrogen**, Analyst **91**, 178 (1966).

Nitrogen oxides (except nitrous oxide), in concentrations above 50 ppm, can be determined by this method. The gas sample is collected in a specially designed evacuated gas bulb. Sulfuric acid and iron sulfate are added to the sample. The per cent transmission of the resulting pink color is read in a spectrophotometer at a wavelength of 520 mμ. The quantity of nitrogen oxides present is read from a calibration curve, and the airborne concentration is calculated.

Interferences

Hydrogen sulfate will interfere with this determination if present in concentrations above 400 ppm.

The method requires approximately 2 hours to complete the analysis. The time is used primarily to prepare the standards for the calibration curve. This method is applicable to process gas analysis and stack gas analysis but is not sensitive enough for industrial hygiene or air pollution work.

Garcia, E. E. **Determination of Nitrite Ion Using the Reaction with *p*-Nitroaniline and Azulene,** Anal. Chem. **13,** 1605 (1967).

The method was not specifically designed for air analysis but appears to be applicable to the analysis of nitrogen oxides. Nitrite ion in excess of 0.22 μg nitrite can be determined by this method. The sample might be collected in a fritted bubbler containing distilled water or possibly sodium hydroxide. An aliquot of the sample containing 1–10 μg of nitrite is quantitatively transferred to a volumetric flask. Solutions of *p*-nitroaniline in acetic acid, azulene in glacial acetic acid, and dilute perchloric acid are added to the sample, which is then diluted to 25 ml. The absorbance of the resulting red-to-purple color is read in a spectrophotometer. The quantity of nitrite present is determined from a calibration curve and the airborne concentration calculated.

Interferences

Iron interferes with this determination.

Applying this method to the determination of nitrogen dioxide should be preceded by some research to ascertain the usefulness of the method.

Dimitriades, B. **Methods for Determining Nitrogen Oxides in Automotive Exhausts,** U.S. Bur. Mines, Rept. Invest. **7133** (1968).

Five procedures for the analysis of nitrogen oxides in automobile exhaust are studied to determine accuracy and applicability to exhaust gas studies. The data show that those methods which convert nitric oxide to nitrogen dioxide before analysis are prone to produce erroneous results because of the instability of nitrogen dioxide. Recommendations for optimum use of these methods are made.

Nitroglycerine

Jacobs, Morris B. *The Analytical Chemistry of Industrial Poisons, Hazards and Solvents,* 2nd ed. (New York: Interscience Publishers, Inc., 1949), p 741.

See Also

Yagoda, H., and F. H. Goldman. J. Ind. Hyg. Toxicol. **25,** 440 (1943).

Nitroglycerine, in the parts per million range, can be determined by this method. The sample can be collected in a midget impinger containing triethylene glycol. After collection, a 5-ml aliquot is quantitatively transferred to a distillation flask, and distilled water, xylenol in triethylene glycol, and sulfuric acid are added. After 10 minutes distilled water is added and the mixture is distilled. The distillate is collected in a small quantity of sodium hydroxide. The yellow color produced is compared with a set of standards prepared from potassium nitrate and the airborne concentration calculated.

Sampling Procedure

The sample can be collected in a midget impinger containing 10 ml of triethylene glycol at a rate of 3 lpm for 20 minutes.

Interferences

This method is not specific for any nitrate ester but can be used for the determination for any one of them.

Analysis requires approximately 2 hours to complete. This method is suitable for industrial hygiene work but is not sufficiently sensitive for air pollution work.

Nitroparaffins

Jones, L. R., and J. A. Reddick. **Colorimetric Determination of Nitroparaffins,** Anal. Chem. **24,** 1533 (1952).

Secondary nitroparaffins, in concentrations above 3 μg in the sample analyzed, can be determined by this method. The sample may be collected in two fritted bubblers containing concentrated sulfuric acid. An aliquot of the sample, up to 10 ml, is quantitatively transferred to a test tube and held in a boiling water bath for 5 minutes. After cooling, resorcinol solution is placed on top of the acid and the sample is mixed slowly. The sample is heated in a water bath and cooled, and the optical density of the resulting red-blue color is read in a spectrophotometer at a wavelength of 560 mμ. The quantity of secondary nitroparaffins present is read from a calibration curve, and the airborne concentration is calculated.

Sampling Procedure

The sample may be collected in two bubblers, series-connected, containing sulfuric acid. A sampling rate of 2 lpm for a period long enough to collect 5–10 μg will provide an adequate sample.

Interferences

Any aliphatic nitroparaffin will interfere with this determination. The method requires approximately 30 minutes to complete. It is suitable for industrial hygiene work, and, if a sufficiently large sample is collected, it is also applicable to air pollution work.

2-Nitropropane

Jones, L. R. **The Determination of 2-Nitropropane in Air,** Am. Ind. Hyg. Assoc. J. **24,** 11 (1963).

2-Nitropropane, in concentrations above 3–5 μg, can be determined by this method. The air sample is collected in a midget fritted bubbler containing 10 ml of concentrated sulfuric acid. The sample is first heated in a water bath and then cooled. Resorcinol reagent is added to the sample, which is again heated in a water bath. The resulting red-blue color is read in a spectrophotometer at a wavelength of 560 mμ. The quantity of 2-nitropropane present is determined from a previously prepared calibration curve.

Sampling Procedure

A sampling rate of 0.5 lpm through the bubbler containing sulfuric acid is sufficient for collection of 2-nitropropane. A 10–30 minute sample should provide sufficient material for analysis.

Interferences

Most secondary aliphatic nitroparaffins as well as most halogenated nitroparaffins will interfere with this method of analysis.

The method is applicable to industrial hygiene work and provides a rapid, accurate method for the determination of 2-nitropropane. Analysis requires approximately 1 hour for completion.

n-Octylamine

Hong, W. H., and K. A. Conners. **Spectrophotometric Determination of Aliphatic Amines by Acylation with Cinnamic Anhydride,** Anal. Chem. **40,** 1273 (1968).

n-Octylamine, in concentrations at the parts per million level, can be determined by this method. This method was not designed specifically for air analysis but appears to be applicable. A 1-ml aliquot of the sample is quantitatively transferred to a 50-ml volumetric flask. Cinnamic anhydride solution and tri-*n*-butylamine in acetonitrile are added, mixed, and allowed to react at room temperature for several minutes. Sodium hydroxide is added to the 50-ml mark and allowed to stand for 10 minutes. The sample mixture is quantitatively transferred to a separatory funnel and extracted with chloroform. The chloroform extract is washed with distilled water and filtered into a 50-ml volumetric flask. The sample is made to volume with chloroform and the absorbance of the sample is read in a spectrophotometer at 274 mμ. The airborne concentration of *n*-octylamine is calculated.

Sampling Procedure

An air sampling procedure must be developed. Collection might be accomplished using a fritted bubbler containing an acetonitrile solution.

Interferences

Any aliphatic amine will interfere with this method.

Olefins

Altshuller, A. P., L. J. Lage, and S. F. Sleva. **Determination of Olefins in Combustion Gases and in the Atmosphere,** Am. Ind. Hyg. Assoc. J. **23,** 289 (1962).

Olefins, in concentrations above 0.1 ppm, can be determined by this method. The sample is collected in a fritted bubbler containing a solution of *p*-dimethylaminobenzaldehyde in glacial acetic acid and concentrated sulfuric acid. Following collection, the sample is heated at

100°C for 20 minutes and then cooled. The absorbance of the sample is read at a wavelength of 500 mμ on a spectrophotometer. The quantity of olefin present is read from a calibration curve and the airborne concentration is calculated as 1-butene. The calibration curve is prepared from 1-butene.

Sampling Procedure

The sampling rate through the fritted bubbler should not exceed 0.3–0.4 lpm. A 10-liter air sample will usually provide enough sample for analysis.

Interferences

Higher alcohols, triophene, and some of the more reactive aromatic hydrocarbons interfere with the method by forming colored reaction products with the sampling solution. Formaldehyde interferes seriously but the interference can be removed by prescrubbing the sample air with a special reagent. Phenol interference can also be removed in the same manner. The interference by nitrogen dioxide can also be removed by pretreating the air sample with ascarite.

The method is quantitative in a range of 0.1–20 ppm and requires approximately 2 hours to complete. It is applicable to automobile exhaust studies. This method is also sufficiently sensitive for ambient air analysis.

Organic Lead

Snyder, L. J. **Determination of Trace Amounts of Organic Lead in Air,** Anal. Chem. **31,** 591 (1967).

A method is provided to analyze organic lead in the parts per trillion range. A special sampling apparatus is used to collect the air sample. The organo-lead is converted to inorganic lead and determined by a dithizone method. A sample of 200 m^3 is collected at a rate of 0.7 cfm. The method requires several hours for completion of analysis but appears to be excellent for air pollution studies.

Ozone (Oxidant)

Smith, R. G., and P. Diamond. **The Microdetermination of Ozone,** Ind. Hyg. Quart. **13,** 235 (1952).

Ozone, in concentrations from 0–10 ppm, can be determined quickly and accurately by this method. The air sample is collected in a gas washing bottle containing 25.0 ml of alkaline potassium iodide solution. Phosphoric acid reagent is added to a 10-ml aliquot of the sample and the mixture is allowed to stand for 5 minutes for cooling to take place. The transmittance of the sample is read at 352 mμ, with water being used in the reference cell. The standard curve is prepared with appropriate concentrations of potassium iodate.

Sampling Procedure

A sampling rate of about 0.5 lpm appears to be satisfactory for the collection of ozone in a gas washing bottle containing 25 ml of absorbing solution.

Interferences

Oxygen does not interfere with the determination. Peroxides do not interfere if the aliquot to be analyzed is boiled. The oxides of nitrogen probably interfere to some slight extent.

The method is quantitative in the range of at least 0–10 μg per ml of solution. The determination is simple and rapid, requiring no special or expensive equipment. The analytical work can be completed in less than 1 hour. This method is suitable for both air pollution and industrial hygiene work.

Todd, G. W. **Modification of Ferrous Thiocyanate Colorimetric Method for the Determination of Some Atmospheric Oxidants,** Anal. Chem. **27,** 1490 (1955).

A method is discussed which is sensitive to oxidants produced by the reaction of ozone with hydrocarbons and much less sensitive to ozone itself. This fact makes the method very useful for air pollution work.

Byers, D. H., and B. E. Saltzman. **Determination of Ozone in Air by Neutral and Alkaline Iodide Procedures,** Am. Ind. Hyg. Assoc. J. **19,** 251 (1958).

The neutral and alkaline iodide methods for the determination of ozone are studied and compared. The advantages and disadvantages of each method are discussed in relation to their use as a field method. Reproducibility of results as well as the factors effecting reproducibility are thoroughly discussed and precautions to be observed are detailed. The effect of some of the interfering substances are described.

Saltzman, B. E., and N. Gilbert. **Iodometric Microdetermination of Organic Oxidants and Ozone. Resolution of Mixtures by Kinetic Colorimetry,** Anal. Chem. **31,** 1914 (1959).

Ozone, in concentrations down to 0.2 ppm, in the absence of other oxidants can be quickly and easily determined by this method. The air sample is collected in neutral iodide reagent in a midget impinger and the color is allowed to develop for 45 minutes. The developed color is read at 352 mμ in a spectrophotometer and compared with a standard curve.

Sampling Procedure

The sampling rate through the impinger containing 10 ml of a neutral iodide reagent is 1 lpm and a 20-liter air sample is sufficient.

Interferences

Sulfur dioxide, oxidants and dust particles on the glassware all cause fading of the color.

The method is quantitative above 2 ppm but is about 0.1 ppm low at an ozone concentration below 2 ppm. This method requires approximately 1.5 hours for complete analysis and is suitable for industrial hygiene work.

Bovee, H. H., and R. J. Robinson. **Sodium Diphenylaminesulfonate as an Analytical Reagent for Ozone,** Anal. Chem. **33,** 1115 (1961).

Ozone, at concentrations well below 0.1 ppm, can be determined with this method. The sample is collected in 1% sodium diphenylaminesulfonate in perchloric acid contained in a midget impinger. The absorbance of the blue color formed is read in a spectrophotometer at 593 mμ. The quantity of ozone is determined by comparison with a calibration curve.

Sampling Procedure

The sampling rate through the impinger containing 10 ml sodium diphenylaminesulfonate in perchloric acid is 0.1 cfm for 10 minutes or until a satisfactory color develops.

Interferences

There is some interference from nitrogen dioxide, chlorine and sulfur dioxide but it is not as serious as with some of the other methods of ozone determination. Most other oxidants which would interfere with the ozone determination have a maximum absorption at wavelengths other than 593 mμ (nitrogen dioxide, chlorine, and hydrogen peroxide). Interferences from these compounds can be minimized by using a narrow band spectrophotometer.

The method is sensitive, requires only a few minutes for analysis, and is suitable for sampling and analysis of the ambient atmosphere. It requires approximately 30 minutes for complete analysis.

Bravo, N. A., and J. P. Lodge, Jr. **Specific Spectrophotometric Determination of Ozone in the Atmosphere,** Anal. Chem. **36,** 671 (1964).

Ozone, in concentrations down to one part per hundred million, can be determined if an 8-liter sample is collected. The air sample is collected in two specially constructed bubblers each containing a solution of 4,4′-dimethoxystilbene in tetrachloroethane. Fluoranthene in chloroform, trifluoroacetic anhydride and trifluoroacetic acid are added to 1 ml of the sampling solution. The absorbance of the resulting blue color is read in a spectrophotometer at 610 mμ. The concentration of ozone is read from a calibration curve.

Sampling Procedure

The sampling rate through the two special bubblers is 0.1–0.15 lpm for 15–60 minutes depending on the expected concentration of ozone.

Interferences

The method appears to be specific for ozone. Hydrogen sulfide has been found to interfere with the color development.

This method has adequate sensitivity for air pollution work.

Regner, V. H. **Measurement of Atmospheric Ozone with the Chemoluminescent Method,** J. Geophys. Res. **69,** 3795 (1964).

Methods are described for the chemoluminescent determination of ozone in the upper atmosphere. A description of the method is detailed for use with a balloon sonde, a surface ozone recorder, and an ozone meter installed in an airplane.

The method appears to be rather specific for ozone but requires frequent calibration because of the effects of light, humidity, etc. on the reagent.

Hendricks, R. H., and L. B. Larsen. **An Evaluation of Selected Methods of Collection and Analysis of Low Concentrations of Ozone,** Am. Ind. Hyg. Assoc. J. **27,** 80 (1966).

Several methods are presented for the determination of ozone. The iodine, phenolphthalein, sodium diphenylamine sulfonate, fluorescien, 4,4'-dimethoxystilbene, and nitrogen dioxide-equivalent methods are discussed in relation to their sensitivity, specificity, advantages, and disadvantages. None of these methods was considered to be completely satisfactory for the analytical determination of ozone. The best results, however, were obtained with the nitrogen dioxide equivalent method.

Hauser, T. R., and D. W. Bradley. **Specific Spectrophotometric Determination of Ozone in the Atmosphere Using 1,2-Di-(4-Pyridyl)ethylene,** Anal. Chem. **38,** 1529 (1966).

Ozone, in concentrations from 0–3.65 μg, can be determined by this method. The air sample is collected in a midget bubbler containing 15 ml of 0.5% 1,2-di-(4-pyridyl)ethylene in glacial acetic acid. A 10-ml aliquot is used for analysis. A 1-ml solution of 3-methyl-2-benzothiazolinone hydrazone hydrochloride is added and the sample is heated in a water bath for 20 minutes. The absorbance of the resulting yellow color is read in a spectrophotometer at 442 mμ. The ozone concentration is calculated from the absorbance-concentration curve simultaneously constructed.

Sampling Procedure

The sampling rate through the bubbler is 0.5 lpm for 0.5–2 hours.

Interferences

There are no known interferences when this procedure is used. The method is considered to be specific for ozone.

The method can be used in both industrial hygiene and air pollution work because of the good sensitivity and specificity for ozone. The analytical procedure requires 1–1.5 hours for completion.

Hauser, T. R., and D. W. Bradley. **Effect of Interfering Substances and Prolonged Sampling on the 1,2-Di-(4-Pyridyl)ethylene Method for Determination of Ozone in Air.** Anal. Chem. **39,** 118 (1967).

This method, after investigation, was found to be useful for sampling ozone for periods up to 24 hours. Interferences which could be expected in atmosphere sampling provided no problem in a 30-minute sampling period and little problem in a 24-hour sampling period.

Jacobs, Morris B. *The Analytical Toxicology of Industrial Inorganic Poisons* (New York: Interscience Publishers, Inc., 1967), p 626.

Atmospheric oxidant, which is considered to be predominately ozone, can be determined in the parts per billion range by this method. The air sample is collected in two large fritted bubblers containing potassium iodide in sodium hydroxide solution. A 25-ml aliquot is quantitatively transferred to a beaker and sulfamic acid solution is added to eliminate the interference by nitrogen oxides. The optical density of the resulting solution is read in a spectrophotometer at 352 mμ. The quantity of ozone present is read from a calibration curve prepared from potassium iodate, and the airborne concentration is calculated.

Sampling Procedure

The air sample is collected in a large fritted bubbler at a rate of 3 lpm for 1 hour.

Interferences

The sulfamic acid removes the interference caused by the presence of nitrogen oxides.

This method requires approximately 1 hour to complete. It is suitable for industrial hygiene and air pollution work.

Jacobs, Morris B. *The Analytical Toxicology of Industrial Inorganic Poisons* (New York: Interscience Publishers, Inc., 1967), p 622.

See Also

1. Smith, R. G., and P. Diamond.   Am. Ind. Hyg. Assoc. J. **13**, 235 (1952).
2. Smith, R. G.   Bur. Ind. Hyg., Detroit Dept. Health (1953).

Atmospheric oxidant, which is considered to be predominately ozone, can be determined in the parts per billion parts of air range by this method. The sample is collected in a Greenburg-Smith impinger containing potassium iodide in a sodium hydroxide solution. After collection, the sample is quantitatively transferred to a beaker and hydrogen peroxide is added to oxidize any' sulfite produced from sulfur dioxide to sulfate. The sample is boiled to remove any excess hydrogen peroxide. The sample is acidified to pH 3.8 with acetic acid to remove the nitrogen oxides as interferences and to liberate iodine formed when ozone is reacted with the absorbing solution. The optical density of the resulting solution is read in a spectrophotometer at a wavelength of 352 mμ. The quantity of ozone or oxidant present is read from a calibration curve prepared from potassium iodate.

Sampling Procedure

The air sample can be collected in Greenburg-Smith impingers containing 75 ml of absorbing solution. A sampling rate of 1 cfm for 30 minutes should be adequate to collect a sample.

Interferences

This determination provides methods for removing sulfur dioxide and nitrogen oxides as interferences.

The method requires approximately 1 hour for complete analysis. It is suitable for industrial hygiene work. The method is also sufficiently sensitive for use in air pollution work.

Deutsch, S. **Acid Potassium Iodide Method for Determining Atmospheric Oxidants**, J.A.P.C.A. **18**, 78 (1968).

Ozone (oxidant), in concentrations above one part per hundred million parts of air, can be determined by this method. The air sample may be collected in a midget impinger containing a solution of potassium iodide, sodium hydroxide, and acetic acid. After collection, the sample is transferred to a graduated cylinder and diluted to 25 ml with distilled water. The absorbance of the resulting solution is read in a spectrophotometer at a wavelength of 355 mμ. The quantity of ozone or oxidant in the sample is determined from a calibration curve prepared from potassium iodate. The airborne concentration of oxidant is then calculated.

Sampling Procedure

The sample can be collected in a midget impinger containing 10 ml absorbing solution. A collection rate of 1–2 lpm is satisfactory. A sampling time of 30 minutes should supply sufficient material for analysis.

Interferences

Hydrogen sulfide and sulfur dioxide do not interfere with this method. Other acid and basic materials may produce some degree of interference.

The method requires approximately 1 hour to complete the analysis. It is sufficiently sensitive for both industrial hygiene and air pollution.

Cohen, I. C., A. F. Smith, and R. Wood. **A Field Method for the Determination of Ozone in the Presence of Nitrogen Dioxide,** Analyst **93,** 507 (1968).

Ozone, in concentrations above 0.05 ppm in a 40-liter air sample, can be determined by this method. The air sample is collected in two midget impingers operating singly. One absorber is equipped with glass wool in the pipet section along with 10 ml neutral buffered potassium iodide. The glass wool removes any ozone present. The second bubbler contains 10 ml neutral buffered potassium iodide solution and determines the quantity of ozone plus nitrogen dioxide. The concentration of ozone is found by determining the optical density of the two sample solutions and converting the results to ozone concentrations by reading from a calibration curve and then subtracting the results of the sample containing nitrogen dioxide from the one containing ozone plus nitrogen dioxide.

Sampling Procedure

The sample may be collected in a midget impinger at a rate of 2 lpm for 20 minutes.

Interferences

Sulfur dioxide reacts with the absorbing solution but this should not invalidate the test because both samples will be affected equally. Metal fumes will interfere with this determination by removing or absorbing ozone.

Analysis requires approximately 30 minutes to complete. The method can be used as a field method in industrial hygiene work but is not sufficiently precise for air pollution work.

Pentachloroethane

Jacobs, M. B. *The Analytical Chemistry of Industrial Poisons, Hazards and Solvents,* 2nd ed. (New York: Interscience Publishers, Inc., 1949), p 565.

See Also

1. Cole, W. H. J. Biol. Chem. **71**, 173 (1926).
2. Gettler, A. O., and H. Blume. Arch. Pathol. **11**, 555 (1931).
3. Ross, J. H. J. Biol. Chem. **58**, 641 (1923/24).

Pentachloroethane in the parts per million range can be determined by this method. The air sample is collected in a bubbler containing 95% ethyl alcohol. After collection, the sample is quantitatively transferred to a volumetric flask and diluted to volume. Pyridine, sodium hydroxide, and an aliquot of the sample are placed in a test tube and heated in a water bath for 1 minute. The resulting color in the pyridine layer is compared with a set of color standards in a color comparator. The permanent color standards are prepared from basic Fuchsin in acidified ethyl alcohol. The concentration of pentachloroethane in air is calculated.

Sampling Procedure

The air sample is collected in a bubbler containing either dilute hydrochloric acid or ethyl alcohol. A sampling rate of 2 lpm for at least 30 minutes should provide an adequate sample.

Interferences

Any material with a 3 halogen-carbon linkage will interfere with this determination. Examples of such compounds are bromoform, iodoform, Chloretone and chloral.

The method requires approximately 1 hour for complete analysis. The method is applicable to industrial hygiene work but is not sufficiently sensitive for air pollution analysis.

Pentanol

Hoare, D. E., and R. R. Ogilvie. **Spectrophotometric Method for the Microdetermination of Monohydric Aliphatic Alcohols,** Anal. Chem. **38**, 1799 (1966).

This method was not designed for air analysis but appears to be applicable for this use. Pentanol in concentrations exceeding approximately 0.1 μg per ml can be determined by this method. The sample may be collected in a midget impinger containing water. An 8-ml aliquot of the sample and an acetate buffer and sodium nitrite solution are quantitatively transferred to a 50-ml flask.

The sample is incubated at 18°C for 30 minutes after which heptane is added. The sample is again incubated at 18°C and agitated. It is cooled at 0°C and transferred to a cold separatory funnel and the aqueous layer is removed. The heptane layer is transferred to a test tube and exposed to calcium chloride to remove water. The sample is reacted with α-naphthylamine and incubated at 18°C for 10 minutes. The color is allowed to develop while the sample is contained in a water bath at 60°C for 30 minutes. After cooling, the absorbance of the resulting solution is read in a spectrophotometer at 550 mμ. The concentration present in the sample is read from a calibration curve, and the airborne concentration is calculated.

Sampling Procedure

The sample may be collected by a fritted bubbler at a rate of 2 lpm. Water may be used as the sampling solution.

Interferences

The method is not specific for monohydric aliphatic alcohols but determines many of them.

The method requires approximately 3 hours for complete analysis and is suitable for industrial hygiene work.

2-Pentanone

Jacobs, Morris B. *The Analytical Chemistry of Industrial Poisons, Hazards and Solvents,* 2nd ed. (New York: Interscience Publishers, Inc., 1949), p 688.

See Also

Patty, F. A. Schrenk, and P. Yant. U.S.P.H.S. Reprint #1702 (1935).

2-Pentanone, in the parts per million range, can be determined by this method. The sample is collected in a flask containing 50 ml of a standardized solution of sodium hydroxide. The flask is equipped with a stopper containing a glass stopcock. The flask is series-connected with a mercurcy U-tube monometer and partially evacuated. After the stopcock is closed, the bottle may be taken to the field and a sample collected by vacuum displacement. The sample volume is then calculated. The ketone is absorbed by the sodium hydroxide and an excess of a standardized iodine solution is added. After 15 minutes the sample is neutralized with sulfuric acid and the excess iodine is titrated with a standardized sodium thiosulfate solution. The quantity of methyl ethyl ketone found must be multiplied by 0.943 to allow for the secondary reactions which occur during the analysis. The airborne concentration can then be calculated.

Interferences

Other ketones as well as any material which is reactive with iodine will interfere.

The method requires approximately 2 hours for completion. The method is suitable for industrial hygiene but is not suitable for air pollution work.

Hashmi, M. H., and A. A. Ayaz. **The Determination of Methyl Ketones and Acetaldehydes by Titration with Hypobromite Using Bordeaux Indicator,** Anal. Chem. **36,** 385 (1964).

2-Pentanone can be simply, accurately and rapidly determined with this method. The method, although not designed for air analysis, should be applicable with some modification. The sample could perhaps be collected in water using an impinger or a fritted bubbler. A measured aliquot of sample is placed in a flask and 3*N* sodium hydroxide is added. The mixture is titrated against standard hypobromite solution using Bordeaux as an internal indicator. The end point shows up as a change from light pink to faint yellow or colorless.

A sampling rate of about 1–2 lpm should be adequate for collection of the sample.

Interferences

Aliphatic aldehydes and methyl ketones will interfere, as will high concentrations of aldehydes.

The method should have application in ambient air, industrial hygiene and stack gas analysis. Analysis should require less than 1 hour to complete.

Perchloroethylene

Hanson, N. W., D. A. Reilly, and H. E. Stagg, Eds. *The Determination of Toxic Substances in Air* (Cambridge, England: W. Heffer and Sons, Ltd., 1965), p 95.

See Also

Brumbaugh, J. H., and D. E. Stallard. J. Agr. Food Chem. 6, 465 (1958).

Perchloroethylene, in concentrations from 10–100 ppm in a 15-liter air sample, can be determined by this method. The air sample is collected in a midget impinger containing 20 ml of a 3:1 mixture of pyridine and aniline. The sample is quantitatively transferred to a reflux apparatus and boiled for 10 minutes. Sodium hydroxide in methanol is added and the solution boiled for another 45 minutes. The sample is cooled, transferred to a flask, and brought to a volume of 50 ml with methyl alcohol. The optical density of the sample is read at 400 mμ, and the quantity of perchloroethylene present is determined from a previously prepared calibration curve. The concentration of perchloroethylene in air is calculated.

The sampling rate through the midget impinger should be about 1 lpm for 15 minutes in order to obtain the sensitivity of 10–100 ppm. Increasing or decreasing the sampling time will increase or decrease the sensitivity range obtainable.

Interferences

Trichloroethylene, chloroform, and carbon tetrachloride will interfere with this determination.

The method is simple and moderately rapid requiring approximately two hours to complete. No special or expensive equipment is needed and the method is applicable to industrial hygiene work. This method is not considered sufficiently sensitive for air pollution work.

Perfluoroisobutylene

Marcoli, K., and A. L. Linch. **Perfluoroisobutylene and Hexafluoropropene Determination in Air,** Am. Ind. Hyg. Assoc. J. **27**, 360 (1966).

Perfluoroisobutylene, in concentrations above 0.1 ppm, can be determined by this method. The air sample is collected in two midget impingers connected in series, each containing methyl alcohol. During sample collection the impingers are cooled in a methanol–dry ice bath. The collected sample is reacted with pyridine and piperidine and allowed to stand for 1 hour. The resulting yellow color is read in a spectrophotometer at 412 mμ. The quantity of perfluoroisobutylene present is determined from a calibration curve, and the airborne concentration is calculated.

Sampling Procedure

A sampling rate below 0.1 cfm is satisfactory for 10–20 minutes. If a 0.1 cubic foot sample is collected, this analytical method will detect 0.10 ppm. This can be improved by collecting longer samples.

Analysis requires 3–4 hours for completion. The preparation of standards is an involved procedure.

Interferences

Hexafluoropropene, tetrafluoroethylene, trifluoroethylene, chlorotrifluoroethylene, 1,1-dichlorodifluoroethylene, and carbon tetrachloride interfere with this determination.

Phenol

Jacobs, Morris B. *The Analytical Chemistry of Industrial Poisons, Hazards and Solvents*, 2nd ed. (New York: Interscience Publishers, Inc., 1949), p 698.

See Also

Scott, R. D. Ind. Eng. Chem. Anal. Ed. 3, 67 (1931).

Phenol in quantities greater than 10 mg can be determined by this method. The sample can be collected in a fritted bubbler or gas washing bottle containing a normal sodium hydroxide solution. After collection, the sample is quantitatively transferred to an Erlenmeyer flask, neutralized and diluted to 200 ml with distilled water. Potassium bromide solution and hydrochloric acid solution are added to the sample which is placed in a water bath at 25°C for 1 hour. Potassium bromate is added and the solution is maintained at 25°C ± 1°C for 1 hour. Potassium iodide is added and after 30 minutes the liberated iodine in the sample is titrated with a standard sodium thiosulfate solution. The airborne concentration of phenol is then calculated.

Sampling Procedures

The sample may be collected in a gas washing bottle containing 50 ml of sodium hydroxide solution at the rate of 0.5 cfm for a period depending upon the expected concentration of phenol.

Interferences

This method will not determine a specific phenol but will determine all phenols. The presence of cresols or aromatic amines will also interfere with the analysis.

The method is suitable for industrial hygiene work but is not sufficiently sensitive for air pollution work.

Jacobs, M. B. *The Analytical Chemistry of Industrial Poisons, Hazards and Solvents.* (New York: Interscience Publishers, Inc., 1949), p 699.

See Also

Gibbs, H. D. J. Biol. Chem. **72**, 649 (1949).

Phenol, in concentrations above 5 μg per liter of solution, can be determined by this method. The sample may be collected in a fritted bubbler containing sodium hydroxide solution. After collection, the sample is diluted so that it contains 5–100 μg of phenol. One or several aliquots of the sample are transferred to Nessler tubes. Alkaline sodium tetraborate solution is added until the pH is approximately 9.6. A solution of 2,6-dibromoquinone-4-chlorimide in alcohol is added to the sample. The blue color is compared after 4–24 hours with a series of standards, and the airborne concentration is calculated.

Sampling Procedure

A fritted bubbler containing 10 ml of a sodium hydroxide solution can be used to collect the sample. A sampling rate of 2–3 lpm for 30 minutes is usually enough to collect a suitable sample.

Interferences

Other phenolic materials as well as chlorine interfere with this analysis. Cresols also will interfere.

The method requires approximately 2 hours for complete analysis except for the time required for color development. Color development requires a minimum of 4 hours and if possible the development should be allowed to continue overnight. The method is suitable for industrial hygiene work, and, if a large enough sample is collected, the method can be used for air pollution work.

Braverman, M. M., S. Hochheiser, and M. B. Jacobs. **Colorimetric Ultramicrodetermination of Phenol in Air,** Am. Ind. Hyg. Assoc. Quart. **18,** 132 (1957).

Phenol, in concentrations ranging from 0.1–1.0 ppb, can be determined by this method. The air sample is collected in a fritted glass bubbler containing a 0.5% solution of sodium bicarbonate. The solution is quantitatively transferred to a separatory funnel, and a few drops of *p*-aminodimethyl aniline sulfate test solution are added to the sample. A 0.1% calcium hypochlorite solution is added until the color in the sample is blue or colorless. After 5 minutes the sample is extracted with chloroform and the resulting solution is allowed to stand for 30 minutes. The optical density is then read at 600 mμ, and the concentration of phenol is calculated from the standard curve.

Sampling Procedure

A sampling rate of 1 cfm through 45 ml of sodium bicarbonate solution contained in a fritted bubbler will collect enough phenol.

Interferences

Hydrogen sulfide may interfere with the method.

The method is rapid, requiring approximately 1 hour to complete, and sensitive to the parts per billion range. Analysis can be carried out in 1–2 hours. The method is applicable to industrial hygiene and air pollution work.

Smith, R. G., J. D. MacEwen, and R. E. Barrow. **Sampling and Analysis of Phenols in Air,** Am. Ind. Hyg. Assoc. J. **20,** 142 (1959).

Phenol, in the parts per billion range, can be determined accurately by this method. The sample is collected in 1N sodium hydroxide. The collected sample is prepared for analysis by the addition of copper sulfate, lowering the pH to less than 4.0 with phosphoric acid and distilling the sample. The distillate is acidified with phosphoric acid, and copper sulfate is added to this solution which is then extracted with sodium chloride and chloroform. The chloroform phase of the solution is extracted with 0.1N sodium hydroxide and diluted to 50 ml. The chloroform remaining in the sample is removed by heating and the sample is ready for analysis. The samples are aliquoted as needed and treated with copper sulfate. The pH is brought to less than 4.0 with phosphoric acid and the sample is distilled. Ammonium chloride is added to the distillate and the pH is adjusted to 10.0. Potassium ferricyanide and 4-aminoantipyrine are added to the sample and extracted with chloroform. The resulting colored solution is read in a spectrophotometer at 460 mμ. Standards are prepared from reagent grade phenol and treated similarly to the samples. The concentration of phenol is determined from the calibration curves.

Sampling Procedure

Samples may be collected in Greenburg-Smith impingers at a rate of 1 cfm, in midget impingers at a rate of 0.1 cfm, or in fritted bubblers at a rate of 0.1 cfm. A sampling duration of 30 minutes is usually sufficient for sample collection.

Interferences

There are no known interferences with this method when used to analyze air samples.

The analytical method is relatively simple but time-consuming; several hours are required to complete an analysis. It is much more economical to analyze several samples simultaneously than it is to analyze one sample. This method is suitable for both industrial hygiene and air pollution work.

Jacobs, Morris B. *The Chemical Analysis of Air Pollutants* (New York: Interscience Publishers, Inc., 1960), p 269.

Phenol, in concentrations above 10 ppb, can be determined by this method. A large fritted gas washing bottle containing a sodium bicarbonate solution may be used to collect the air sample. After collection, the sample is quantitatively transferred to a separatory funnel, *p*-aminodimethylaniline sulfate solution is added, and a pink color becomes visible. Enough calcium hypochlorite solution is added to change the color of the sample solution to blue or colorless. After 5 minutes the sample is extracted with chloroform and allowed to stand for 30 minutes. The optical density of the solution is read in a spectrophotometer at a wavelength of 600 mμ. The quantity of phenol in the sample is determined from a calibration curve and the airborne concentration calculated.

Sampling Procedure

The sample may be collected in a gas washing bottle containing 45–50 ml sodium bicarbonate solution at a flow rate of 1 cfm. A sampling duration of 15–30 minutes should collect a sufficient sample for analysis.

Interferences

The method is not specific for any particular phenol but will determine total phenolic compounds.

The method requires approximately 1.5 hours to complete, and the technique is suitable for both industrial hygiene and air pollution work.

Papariello, G. J., and M. A. Janish. **Diphenylpicrylhydrazyl as an Organic Analytical Reagent in the Spectrophotometric Analysis of Phenol,** Anal. Chem. **38,** 211 (1966).

Phenols, at concentrations above 10^{-3}–10^{-5} ;..illimoles per sample, can be determined by this method. A 4-ml portion is used for analysis. Methanol, acetate buffer solution, and diphenylpiᶜrylhydrazyl reagent are added to the sample. A reagent blank is prepared separately. The absorbance of sample and reagent blank is read at 515 mμ in a spectrophotometer. The difference in absorbance is obtained and the phenol concentration is read from a calibration curve of absorbance difference versus concentration.

This method has not as yet been adapted to air analysis but it appears to be suitable. A collection method must be devised.

The method determines total phenols and does not require a long time to complete the analysis.

Interferences

Aromatic amines and mercaptans may interfere.

o-Phenylenediamine

Stewart, J. T., T. D. Shaw, and A. B. Ray. **Spectrophotometric Determination of Primary Aromatic Amines with 9-Chloroacridine,** Anal. Chem. **41,** 360 (1969).

This method was not designed for air analysis but appears to be modifiable for this use. Most of these amines have some vapor pressure; therefore this analysis is abstracted here.

o-Phenylenediamine in concentrations above 10^{-7} moles can be determined by this method. The sample can probably be collected in ethyl alcohol. After collection a 1-ml aliquot of the amine is quantitatively transferred to a volumetric flask. A solution of 9-chloroacridine is added and the pH is adjusted to 4.0 with hydrochloric acid. The absorbance of the resulting orange-colored solution is read in a spectrophotometer at 435 mμ.

Sampling Procedure

The sample may be collected in a fritted bubbler at a rate of 2 lpm.

Interferences

Primary amines and acridone will interfere with this determination. The method requires approximately 1 hour for analysis. It is suitable for industrial hygiene work.

Phosgene

Linch, A. L., S. S. Lord, Jr., K. A. Kubitz, and M. R. De-Brunner. **Phosgene in Air Development of Improved Detection Procedures,** Am. Ind. Hyg. Assoc. J. **26,** 465 (1965).

Methods for the determination of phosgene in air at concentrations ranging from 0.02–10 ppm are reviewed and discussed.

One method involves hydrolysis of phosgene, producing hydrochloric acid as one of the end products which can be analytically determined by means of an indicator. Silver nitrate can also be used to determine the chloride produced by the hydrolysis of phosgene. These methods, however, are not specific for phosgene. Because the chloride ion is present in many industrial environments, these methods are therefore not satisfactory.

Iodometric methods have also been applied to the analysis of phosgene but these methods again lack specificity. The sensitivity is also relatively poor and trace amounts cannot be determined by this method.

Gravimetric procedures have also been used for the analysis of phosgene. The phosgene is reacted with aniline producing the insoluble diphenylurea as one of the products. This material can be weighted and calculated as phosgene. The problem with this method is that concentrations above 10 ppm can be determined but lower concentrations cannot because results are erratic and unreliable.

Colorimetric methods of analysis have also been used to determine phosgene quantitatively. One of these involves the impregnation of paper with diphenylamine and 4-dimethylaminobenzaldehyde. Phosgene, when in contact with this reagent, produces a yellow color. The method is sensitive to 1 ppm but the papers are affected by light. Oxygen, chlorine, and hydrochloric acid also interfere. Paper impregnated with 4-dimethylaminobenzaldehyde and *N*-alkylanilines will produce blue colorations at concentrations of around 0.25 ppm phosgene. Several other similar methods are also briefly described. There are 48 references cited.

Jacobs, Morris B.   *The Analytical Toxicology of Industrial Inorganic Poisons* (New York: Interscience Publishers, Inc., 1967), p 650.
See Also
Liddel, H. F.   Analyst **82**, 375 (1957).

Phosgene, in concentrations exceeding approximately 0.5 ppm, can be determined by this method if a 1-liter air sample is collected. A reagent paper is prepared by impregnation with a solution of *N*-ethyl-1-hydroxyethylaniline, *p*-dimethylaminobenzaldehyde, and diethyl phthalate in ethyl alcohol. Air is drawn through the impregnated filter paper until the blue color of phosgene is detected. The color produced is compared with a series of color standards, and the airborne concentration is calculated.

Jacobs, M. B.   *The Analytical Toxicology of Industrial Inorganic Poisons* (New York: Interscience Publishers, Inc., 1967), p 649.
See Also
Dept. Sci. Ind. Res. British Leaflet **8** (1939).

Phosgene, in concentrations from 0.5–2.0 ppm, can be determined by this method. The air sample is drawn through a known area of an impregnated filter paper using a pump which delivers a known air volume. The filter is impregnated with a solution of diphenylamine and *p*-dimethylaminobenzaldehyde. The yellow-to-orange coloration of the sample is compared with a series of 5 colors on a color chart and the concentration of phosgene is calculated.

Interferences

Chlorine and hydrogen chloride will interfere with this determination.

Analysis requires only a few minutes to complete. This method is suitable for industrial hygiene work.

Phosphine

Hughes, J. G., and A. T. Jones. **The Estimation of Phosphine in Air,** Am. Ind. Hyg. Assoc. J. **24,** 164 (1963).

Phosphine, at concentrations above 0.02 ppm, can be estimated with this method. Filter paper is impregnated with 0.1N silver nitrate solution and allowed to dry. The air is passed through the paper. A piston pump with a capacity of 100–200 ml per minute is used as the vacuum source. Sufficient air must be drawn through the impregnated paper to produce a definite spot. The stain is removed from the filter paper with hot nitric acid and the resulting solution is neutralized to phenolphthalein with sodium hydroxide. Sodium sulfide and boric acid are added, and the sample is diluted to 50 ml and read in a spectrophotometer at 470 mμ. The quantity of silver present is read from a calibration curve constructed from solutions containing known concentrations of silver nitrate. It is also possible to construct known visual standards.

This method is applicable to industrial hygiene work to determine whether or not the threshold limit value for phosphine has been exceeded. Analysis requires about 1 hour for completion.

Dechant, R., G. Sanders, and R. Graul. **The Determination of Phosphine in Air,** Am. Ind. Hyg. Assoc. J. **27,** 75 (1966).

Phosphine, in concentrations above 0.05 ppm, can be determined quickly and accurately by this method. The air sample is collected in a fritted bubbler preceded by a lead acetate trap to remove hydrogen sulfide. The fritted bubbler contains 10 ml of a silver diethyldithiocarbamate in pyridine solution. The reddish color produced by this reaction is read at a wavelength of 465 mμ. This analysis can be completed in the field.

The sampling rate should be maintained at a rate below 0.5 lpm to ensure adequate collection efficiency.

Interferences

Arsine, stibine, and hydrogen sulfide are known to interfere with this method of analysis. The hydrogen sulfide interference can be removed by introducing a lead acetate trap in front of the fritted bubbler.

This method can be used in industrial hygiene work and requires approximately 30 minutes per sample. A procedure for constructing a calibration curve is also presented. This requires approximately 2 hours.

Polymethylenepolyphenyl Isocyanate (PAPI)

Meddle, D. W., D. W. Radford, and R. Wood. **A Field Method for the Determination of Organic Aromatic Isocyanates in Air,** Analyst **94,** 369 (1969).

Polymethylenepolyphenyl isocyanate (PAPI) in concentrations from 0.0–0.4 ppm, can be determined by this method. The sample is collected in a small fritted bubbler containing dimethylformamide in dilute hydrochloric acid. After collection, a solution of sodium nitrite and bromide, sulfamic acid and N-1-naphthylethylenediamine is added to the sample. The resulting color is compared with color standards or the absorbance is read in a spectrophotometer. The concentration of isocyanate is then calculated.

Sampling Procedure

The air sample is collected in a small bubbler at a rate of 1 lpm for 10 minutes. This procedure should provide sufficient sample for analysis.

Interferences

Other isocyanates and any primary amine will interfere with this determination.

The method requires approximately 45 minutes for complete analysis. The procedure is applicable to both industrial hygiene and air pollution work.

Propionaldehyde

Ruch, J. E., and J. B. Johnson. **Determination of Aldehydes by Mercurimetric Oxidation,** Anal. Chem. **28,** 69 (1956).

Propionaldehyde, in the parts per million range, can be determined by this method. This method is not designed for air analysis and a sampling procedure must be devised. The sample is quantitatively transferred to an Erlenmeyer flask and 50 ml of a solution of potassium iodide in potassium hydroxide are added. The sample is kept cool in an ice bath. Then 50 ml of agar and 25 ml of glacial acetic acid are added.

A standardized iodine solution is added and after 15 minutes the sample is titrated with standardized thiosulfate solution. The quantity of aldehyde present is then calculated.

Sampling Procedure

No air sampling procedure has yet been developed.

Interferences

Alcohol and esters interfere slightly with this determination. Some vinyl compounds, unsaturated aldehydes, acetone and methyl ethyl ketone also interfere slightly.

Sawicki E., T. R. Hauser, T. W. Stanely, and W. Elbert. **The 3-Methyl-2-Benzothiazolone Hydrozone Test. Sensitive New Methods for the Detection, Rapid Estimation and Determination of Aliphatic Aldehydes,** Anal. Chem. 33, 93 (1961).

Propionaldehyde can be analyzed in quantities as low as 5 μg per 100 ml of solution. Propionaldehyde, and other aliphatic aldehydes, can be determined specifically if only one of these compounds is present in the contaminated air.

Air is sampled through an impinger containing a collecting solution of 10 ml 3-methyl-2-benzothiazolone and distilled water. The solution is transferred to a volumetric flask and aqueous ferric chloride is added. The mixture is then diluted to 100 ml with acetone. The absorbance of the resulting blue color is read in a spectrophotometer at 670 mμ and the quantity of aldehyde present is read from a calibration curve.

Sampling Procedure

A sampling rate of 2 lpm through a midget impinger containing 10 ml of solution should be satisfactory for collection of the aldehyde.

Interferences

Other aliphatic aldehydes interfere and if they exist singly in the air to be sampled they can be accurately determined by this method. Also thought to interfere are aniline, N-alkylanilines, N,N-dialkylanilines, indoles, carbazoles, and phenothiazines.

The method is quantitative for acetaldehyde from a concentration of 5–125 μg per 100 ml of solution. The method is applicable to air and auto exhaust analysis and requires approximately 30 minutes to complete.

Albrecht, A. M., W. I. Scher, Jr., and H. J. Vogel. **Determination of Aliphatic Aldehydes by Spectrophotometry,** Anal. Chem. **34,** 398 (1962).

Propionaldehyde can be determined quantitatively at concentrations below 0.4 moles per ml of sampling solution. The air sample may be collected in a midget impinger containing 10 ml of distilled water. To an aliquot of this sample is added a solution of methylamine hydrochloride in sodium pyrophosphate followed by the addition of a solution of *o*-aminobenzaldehyde. The absorbance of the yellow-colored reaction mixture is read at 440 mμ in a spectrophotometer. The quantity present is read from a calibration curve.

The sampling rate may be 0.1 cfm through a midget impinger or 1 cfm through a standard impinger. Scrubbers or gas washing bottles may be used. A sampling duration of 30 minutes will usually collect a suitable sample.

Interferences

Other aliphatic aldehydes interfere and many of them can be determined by this method.

The method is useful for atmospheric sampling and analysis and should be adaptable for use at stack concentrations. Analysis requires approximately 1 hour.

Kwan, T. W., and B. M. Watts. **A New Color Reaction of Anthrone with Malonaldehyde and Other Aliphatic Aldehydes,** Anal. Chem. **35,** 733 (1963).

A method is described for the analysis of propionaldehyde using anthrone as the color-forming reagent. The method appears to be applicable to air samples containing elevated concentrations of the aldehyde. More work needs to be done to determine sampling solutions, sampling rates, and sensitivities before the method can be used routinely.

Propyl Acetate

Goddu, R. F., N. F. Le Blanc, and C. M. Wright. **Spectrophotometric Determination of Esters and Anhydrides by Hydroxamic Acid Reaction,** Anal. Chem. **27,** 1251 (1955).

See Also

Hill, V. T.   Ind. Eng. Chem., Anal. Ed. **18**, 317 (1946).

Propyl acetate, in concentrations above approximately 20 ppm in a 25-liter air sample, can be determined by this method. The sample is collected in two fritted bubblers connected in series, each containing ethyl alcohol. The sample is reacted with an alkaline hydroxylamine solution. The addition of ferric ion to this mixture produces a highly colored product. The absorbance of this product is read at a wavelength of 530 mμ. The quantity of ester present is read from a calibration curve and the airborne concentration is calculated.

Sampling Procedure

The air sample may be collected in two fritted bubblers connected in series, each containing 10 ml ethyl alcohol. The sampling rate should be approximately 1–2 lpm until at least 25 liters of air have been sampled.

Interferences

Any other esters, anhydrides, aldehydes, and isocyanates will interfere with this determination.

This method requires approximately 2 hours for complete analysis. It is applicable to industrial hygiene work but is not sufficiently sensitive for air pollution work.

Propyl Alcohol

Jaselskis, B., and J. P. Warriner.   **Titrimetric Determination of Primary and Secondary Alcohols by Xenon Trioxide Oxidation,** Anal. Chem. **38**, 563 (1966).

Propyl alcohol, in concentrations above 30 μg, can be determined by this method. An aliquot of the sample containing at least 30 μg of alcohol is quantitatively transferred to an Erlenmeyer flask. The sample is diluted to 20 ml and a known quantity of xenon trioxide standard solution is added. After two hours, several drops of sulfuric acid and sodium iodide are added to liberate the triiodide ion. The quantity of xenon trioxide used during the oxidation equals the difference between the xenon trioxide before reaction and after reaction with the alcohol.

The quantity of alcohol present is determined from a calibration curve, and the airborne concentration is calculated.

Sampling Procedure

The sample may be collected in a fritted bubbler containing distilled water at a rate of 2.8 lpm for a period long enough to collect 30 μg.

Interferences

Halides, amines, carboxylic acids, ketones, and aldehydes interfere with this determination.

Analysis requires approximately 4 hours to complete. The method is suitable for industrial hygiene analysis but is probably not sensitive enough for air pollution work.

Hoare, D. E., and R. R. Ogilvie. **Spectrophotometric Method for the Microdetermination of Monohydric Aliphatic Alcohols,** Anal. Chem. 38, 1799 (1966).

This method was not designed for air analysis but appears to be applicable. Propyl alcohol in concentrations exceeding 0.1 μg per ml can be determined by this method. The sample may be collected in a midget impinger containing water. An 8-ml aliquot of the sample along with an acetate buffer and sodium nitrite solution are quantitatively transferred to a 50-ml flask.

The sample is incubated at 18°C for 30 minutes after which heptane is added. The sample is again incubated at 18°C and agitated. It is cooled to 0°C and transferred to a cold separatory funnel and the aqueous layer removed. The heptane layer is transferred to a test tube and exposed to calcium chloride to remove water. The sample is reacted with α-naphthylamine and incubated at 18°C for 10 minutes. The color is allowed to develop while the sample is contained in a water bath at 60°C for 30 minutes. After cooling, the absorbance of the resulting solution is read in a spectrophotometer at 550 mμ. The concentration present in the sample is read from a calibration curve, and the airborne concentration is calculated.

Sampling Procedure

The sample may be collected by a fritted bubbler at a rate of 2 lpm. Water may be used as the sampling solution.

Interferences

The method is not specific for monohydric aliphatic alcohols but determines many of them.

Analysis requires approximately 3 hours to complete and is suitable for industrial hygiene work.

Propylamine

Scherberger, R. F., F. H. Miller, and D. W. Fasset. **The Determination of N-Butylamine in Air**, Am. Ind. Hyg. Assoc. J. **21**, 471 (1960).

Propylamine, in concentrations above 0.1 ppm in a one cubic foot air sample, can be determined by this method. The air sample is collected is a gas washing bottle or midget fritted bubbler containing a solution of concentrated hydrochloric acid and isopropyl alcohol. An aliquot of less than 3 ml is used for analysis. Pyridine and ninhydrin in isopropyl alcohol are added to the sample which is then heated in a water bath for 7 minutes. The sample is next cooled for 10 minutes in a cold water bath. The absorbance of the resulting solution is read in a spectrophotometer at 575 mμ. The concentration of propylamine in the sample is determined from a calibration curve, and the airborne concentration is calculated.

Sampling Procedure

A sampling rate of 0.1 cfm for periods upwards of 10 minutes is satisfactory for collection of the amine if a fritted midget bubbler is used.

Interferences

The method is not specific for any one amine and other amines will interfere.

The determination is simple and rapid, requiring approximately 2 hours for completion. This method is applicable to industrial hygiene work and in some cases to air pollution analysis.

Hong, W. H., and K. A. Conners. **Spectrophotometric Determination of Aliphatic Amines by Acylation with Cinnamic Anhydride**, Anal. Chem. **40**, 1273 (1968).

n-Propylamine, in concentrations at the parts per million level, can be determined by this method. This method was not designed specifically for air analysis but appears to be applicable. A 1-ml aliquot of the sample is quantitatively transferred to a 50-ml volumetric flask. Cinnamic anhydride solution and tri-*n*-butylamine in acetonitrile are added, mixed and allowed to react at room temperature for several minutes. Sodium hydroxide is added to the 50 ml mark and allowed to stand for 10 minutes. The sample mixture is quantitatively transferred to a separatory funnel and extracted with chloroform. The chloroform extract is washed with distilled water and filtered into a 50-ml volumetric flask. The sample is made to volume with chloroform and the absorbance of the sample is read in a spectrophotometer at 274 mμ. The airborne concentration of *n*-propylamine is calculated.

Sampling Procedure

An air sampling procedure must be developed. Collection might be accomplished using a fritted bubbler containing an acetonitrile solution.

Interferences

Any aliphatic amine will interfere with this method.

Propylene Glycol

Wise, H., T. T. Puck, and H. M. Stral.   **A Rapid Colorimetric Method for the Determination of Glycols in Air,** J. Biol. Chem. **150,** 61 (1943).

Propylene glycol, in the parts per million range, can be determined by this method. The sample is collected in two series-connected Folin tubes immersed in a test tube containing distilled water. After collection, an aliquot of the sample is quantitatively transferred to a large test tube which is immersed in cold water. Ten ml of a potassium dichromate in sulfuric acid solution is added and the sample is heated in a boiling water bath for 15 minutes. The intensity of the resulting green color is read in a colorimeter at a wavelength of 616 mμ. The quantity of propylene glycol is determined from a calibration curve, and the airborne concentration is calculated.

Sampling Procedure

A flow rate of 20–30 lpm is satisfactory. Collection must be timed to obtain at least a 50-liter sample.

Interferences

Any reducing material will interfere with this determination.

The method requires less than 2 hours for complete analysis and is suitable for industrial hygiene work. This method is probably not suitable for air pollution work because of the long sampling time that would be required and because of interferences that would be present.

Pyridine

Higson, H. G., R. F. Raimondo, and E. W. Tunstall. **Spectrophotometric Determination of Pyridine in Aromatic Hydrocarbons with *p*-Phenyenediamine,** Anal. Chem 41, 1474 (1969).

This method, although not designed for air analysis, can be modified for this use. Pyridine, in concentrations above approximately 10 μg per ml, can be determined by this method. The air sample may be collected in benzene, toluene or xylene. After collection, the sample is extracted twice with hydrochloric acid. A phthalate buffer is added to the extracted sample which is then diluted to 100 ml with distilled water. An aliquot no larger than 3 ml is quantitatively transferred to a flask and diluted to 25 ml with distilled water. First cyanogen bromide and then 15 minutes later a *p*-phenylenediamine solution are added to the flask. After 3 minutes the absorbance of the resulting orange-colored solution is read in a spectrophotometer at a wavelength of 480 mμ.

Sampling Procedure

The sample can be collected in a midget impinger containing 10 ml benzene, toluene or xylene. A sampling rate of 2 lpm should be used for a duration sufficient to collect approximately 10 μg of pyridine.

Interferences

Zinc, iron, nickel, copper, and thiocyanate will interfere with this determination.

The method requires approximately 1 hour for complete analysis. It is suitable for industrial hygiene work provided that a sufficiently long sampling time is used.

Stibine

Webster, H., and L. T. Farihall. **The Microdetermination of Stibine,**
J. Ind. Hyg. Toxicol. **27,** 183 (1945).

Stibine, in concentrations from 0.2–80 μg, can be determined by this
method. The air sample is collected in a bubbler containing 20 ml of
mercuric chloride solution. A 100-ml sample is collected. Ceric sulfate
in hydrochloric acid is added to the solution to oxidize any antimony
from the +3 to the +5 valence state. Hydroxylamine hydrochloride is
added to remove the excess ceric sulfate and the Rhodamine B reagent
is added to develop the color. The Rhodamine–antimony complex is
extracted with benzene and the optical density is read in a spectrophotometer at 565 mμ. The concentration of stibine is read from a calibration curve.

Interferences

Bromine, chromium, iodine, silver, thallium, and tungsten all interfere with the determination.

The method is applicable to industrial hygiene and stack gas analysis.
Analysis requires about 2 hours to complete.

Holland, R. **The Determination of Stibine,** Analyst **87,** 385 (1962).

Stibine, in concentrations above 10 μg per 10 ml of sampling solution, can be determined by this method. The sample can be collected
in a fritted bubbler containing a solution of iodine, sulfuric acid and
potassium iodide. After collection, the solution is reacted with sodium
hypophosphite to reduce the excess iodine. The optical density of the
resulting solution is determined at a wavelength of 330 mμ. The quantity of stibine present in the sample is read from a calibration curve
prepared using antimony.

Sampling Procedure

The sample can be collected in a fritted bubbler containing 10 ml of
the sampling solution. A sampling rate of 2 lpm for 15–30 minutes
should collect an adequate sample.

Interferences

Any material reacting with iodine will interfere with this determination.

The method requires approximately 30 minutes to complete the analysis. This technique is not sensitive enough for industrial hygiene work but can be used to determine the quantity of stibine in process gases.

Hanson, N. W., D. A. Reilly, and H. E. Stagg, Eds. *The Determination of Toxic Substances in Air* (Cambridge, England: W. Heffer and Sons, Ltd., 1965), p 179.

See Also
1. Holland, R.   Chem. Age (London) **80**, 721 (1958).
2. McChesney, E. W.   Ind. Eng. Chem., Anal. Ed. **18**, 146 (1946).

Stibine, in concentrations from 0.05–0.80 ppm in a 40-liter air sample, can be determined by this method. The air sample is collected in a gas washing bottle containing 25 ml of a solution of potassium iodide and iodine in sulfuric acid. After collection, the sample is quantitatively transferred to a 25-ml flask and an ascorbic acid solution is added. The sample is diluted to 25 ml with distilled water. The optical density of the resulting yellow-colored solution is read in a spectrophotometer at a wavelength of 425 mμ. The quantity of stibine in the sample is read from a calibration curve prepared from antimony, and the airborne concentration of stibine is calculated.

The sampling rate through the gas washing bottle should be approximately 2 lpm for a period long enough to collect at least 40 liters of air.

Interferences

Antimony in any form will interfere with this analytical method.

The method is simple and requires approximately 1 hour to complete. No special or expensive equipment is required. This method is suitable for industrial hygiene and air pollution work.

Styrene

Rowe, V. K., G. V. Atchison, E. A. Luce, and E. M. Adams.   **The Determination of Monomeric Styrene in Air**, J. Ind. Hyg. **25**, 348 (1943).

Three methods for the determination of monomeric styrene are presented. The ultraviolet method can accurately determine concentrations above 0.01% in methanol. The infrared method is applicable to concentrations above 0.05% in carbon disulfide or carbon tetrachloride (sampling solutions). The nitration method is applicable to concentrations from 0–5.0 mg in water, benzene or ethylbenzene.

Sampling procedures and analytical techniques are described for the sampling and analysis of monomeric styrene.

Jacobs, Morris B. *The Analytical Chemistry of Industrial Poisons, Hazards and Solvents,* 2nd ed. (New York: Interscience Publishers, Inc., 1949), p 549.

See Also
1. Schrenk, H. H., S. J. Pearce, and W. P. Yant, U.S. Bur. Mines. Rept. Invest. 3287 (1935).
2. Pearce, S. J., H. H. Schrenk, and W. P. Yant, U.S. Bur. Mines, Rept. Invest. 3302 (1936).

Styrene, in concentrations above approximately 25 ppm can be determined by this method if a 0.5-liter air sample is collected. This limit can be extended by increasing the sampling time significantly. The air sample is collected by sampling through a special bubbler which contains a nitrating acid composed of equal quantities of concentrated sulfuric acid and fuming nitric acid. After collection, the sample is allowed to react 30 minutes to ensure complete nitration. The sample is quantitatively transferred to an Erlenmeyer flask and cooled below 20°C. The sample is neutralized by adding sodium hydroxide slowly and carefully. The solution is warmed to 30°C, and 10 ml of methyl ethyl ketone (butanone) is added. The sample is transferred to a separatory funnel and the water drawn off. Sodium hydroxide is added and the color is allowed to develop for 1 hour. The resulting green color is compared with a set of standards and the quantity present in the sample is determined. The airborne concentration is calculated.

Sampling Procedure

The sample may be collected in a special bubbler containing nitrating acid. A sampling rate of 30 ml per minute for approximately 1 hour should provide a sufficient sample for analysis.

Interferences

Toluene, benzene, ethylbenzene, chlorobenzene, and xylene will interfere with this determination.

The method requires approximately 3 hours for analysis. If a 60-minute sample is collected, the method is suitable for industrial hygiene but is not sufficiently sensitive for air pollution work.

Jacobs, Morris B. *The Analytical Chemistry of Industrial Poisons, Hazards and Solvents,* 2nd ed. (New York: Interscience Publishers, Inc., 1949), p 548.

See Also

Rowe, V. K., J. Atchison, E. N. Luce, and E. M. Adams. J. Ind. Hyg. Toxicol. **25,** 348 (1943).

Styrene (vinyl benzene) in the parts per million range can be determined by this method. The sample is collected in a bubbler containing glass beads submerged in carbon tetrachloride. After collection, the sample is quantitatively transferred to an Erlenmeyer flask. If the presence of butadiene is suspected, the sample must be heated to 80°C for 20 minutes in a water bath. After cooling, the sample is nitrated with a mixture of concentrated sulfuric and nitric acid. The sample is diluted with water and quantitatively transferred to a separatory funnel. The carbon tetrachloride layer is then removed and discarded. The sample is further diluted with water and the transmission is measured using a B-42 filter. The quantity of styrene present in the sample is determined from a calibration curve, and the airborne concentration is calculated.

Sampling Procedure

The sample is collected in a bubbler containing glass beads submerged in carbon tetrachloride at a rate of 1 lpm for 30 minutes.

Interferences

Other benzene derivatives are likely to interfere with this method of analysis. The method requires approximately 1.5 hours for analysis. This method is suitable for industrial hygiene work but is not sufficiently sensitive for air pollution work.

Hanson, N. W., D. A. Reilly, and H. E. Stagg, Eds. *The Determination of Toxic Substances in Air* (Cambridge, England: W. Heffer and Sons, Ltd., 1965), p 182.

See Also

Rowe, V. K., G. L. Atchison, E. N. Luce, and E. M. Adams. J. Ind. Hyg. Toxicol. **25,** 348 (1943).

Styrene, in concentrations from 25–250 ppm in a 5-liter air sample, can be determined by this method. The air sample is collected in a midget impinger containing carbon tetrachloride. After collection, the sample is quantitatively transferred to an Erlenmeyer flask and a mixture of sulfuric and nitric acid is added. After 10 minutes the sample is transferred to a separatory funnel and the carbon tetrachloride layer is discarded. The optical density of the resulting yellow-colored solution is read in a spectrophotometer at 400 mμ, and the quantity of styrene present in the sample is read from a previously prepared calibration curve. The airborne concentration is calculated.

The sampling rate through the midget impinger should be approximately 1 lpm for at least 5 minutes.

Interferences

The method appears to be relatively specific for styrene.

The method is simple and requires approximately 1.5 hours to complete the analysis. No special or expensive equipment is required. This method is suitable for industrial hygiene work.

Hanson, N. W., D. A. Reilly, and H. E. Stagg, Eds.   *The Determination of Toxic Substances in Air* (Cambridge, England: W. Heffer and Sons, Ltd., 1965), p 181.

Styrene, in concentrations from 25–200 ppm in a 1-liter air sample, can be determined by this method. The air sample is collected in a midget impinger containing ethyl alcohol. After collection, the optical density of the sample is read in a spectrophotometer at a wavelength of 290 mμ. The quantity of styrene present in the sample is read from a previously prepared calibration curve, and the airborne concentration is calculated.

The rate through the midget impinger should be approximately 0.5 lpm. The analytical range of the determination can be extended by increasing or decreasing the volume of air sampled.

Interferences

This method is not specific for styrene and any material absorbing at 290 mμ will interfere.

The method is simple and requires approximately 15 minutes for complete analysis. No special or expensive equipment is required. This method is suitable for industrial hygiene work.

Sulfates

Bertolacini, R. J., and J. E. Barney. **Ultraviolet Spectrophotometric Determination of Sulfate, Chloride and Fluoride with Chloranilic Acid,** Anal. Chem. **30,** 202 (1958).

Sulfates in concentrations above 0.06 ppm can be determined by this method. The method is applicable to the determination of sulfur dioxide when this gas is converted to sulfate ion during or after collection. The air sample may be collected in midget impingers containing distilled water. The sample is passed through a column containing Dowex 50 x 8 resin, in the hydrogen form, to remove interfering cations. The pH of the solution is adjusted to 7.0 and a potassium acid phthalate buffer is added. Finally a barium chloranilate buffer is added and the sample is filtered. The absorbance of the filtrate is read in a spectrophotometer at 332 mμ. The quantity of sulfate present is read from a calibration curve, and the airborne concentration is calculated.

Sampling Procedure

A sampling rate of 0.1 cfm through a midget impinger containing 10 ml distilled water should be satisfactory for collection.

Interferences

Interferences are negligible with this procedure.

The method can be used in air pollution work as well as areas where higher concentrations are known to exist. Analysis requires about 30 minutes to complete.

Sulfur Dioxide

Stang, A. M., J. E. Zatek, and C. D. Robson. **A Colorimetric Method for the Determination of Sulfur Dioxide in Air,** Am. Ind. Hyg. Assoc. J. **12,** 5 (1951).

Sulfur dioxide, in concentrations above 1 μg per 5 ml of collecting solution, can be determined by this method. The air sample can be collected in either a Greenburg-Smith impinger containing 100 ml of collecting solution or a midget impinger containing 10 ml of collecting solution. The collecting solution consists of sodium hydroxide containing a small quantity of glycerine. A 5-ml aliquot is placed in a previously darkened volumetric flask, 2 ml of the color-forming solution is added, and the mixture is diluted to 25 ml with distilled water. The color forming reagent consists of a mixture of basic Fuchsin in ethyl alcohol, formaldehyde and sulfuric acid. The sample is shaken and allowed to stand for exactly 15 minutes before the color is read in a spectrophotometer at a wavelength of 525 mμ. The color produced is compared with the colors produced in a set of standards made from sodium metabisulfite.

Sampling Procedure

The sampling rate is 1 cfm using the Greenburg-Smith impinger and 0.1 cfm when using the midget impinger.

Interferences

Hydrogen sulfide produces some interferences. It is also possible that some other sulfur compounds also interfere.

The method is quantitative, simple, rapid, and requires no special or expensive equipment. The color-forming solution does have to be aged for 3 days. The rest of the analysis requires 1–2 hours for completion. The method is suitable for both industrial hygiene and air pollution analysis.

Jacobs, M. B. **Techniques for Measurement of Hydrogen Sulfide and Sulfur Oxides,** Nat. Acad. Sci., Nat. Res. Council, Geophy. Monograph #3 (1959), p 24.

Several methods for the determination of sulfur dioxide are discussed in detail. These are the West and Gaeke disulfitomercurate method, the hydrogen peroxide method, the iodine method, the iodine thiosulfate method, the conductivity method, and the lead peroxide cylinder method.

Welch, A. F., and J. P. Terry, M. P. H. **Developments in the Measurements of Atmospheric Sulfur Dioxide,** Am. Ind. Hyg. Assoc. J. **21,** 316 (1960).

The sodium tetrachloromercurate method of West and Gaeke for sulfur dioxide is investigated and compared with the Thomas autometer automatic recording instrument, the peroxide candle and the hydrogen peroxide methods. Data from this research indicated that the sodium tetrachloromercurate method was accurate and very sensitive. This method produces the same results as those obtained with the Thomas autometer. A mathematical relationship is established between the hydrogen peroxide method and the sodium tetrachloromercurate method.

Stephens, B. G., and F. Lindstrom. **Spectrophotometric Determination of Sulfur Dioxide Suitable for Atmospheric Analysis,** Anal. Chem. **36,** 1308 (1964).

Sulfur dioxide, in concentrations from 0.05–2500 μg, can be determined by this method. The sample is collected in a gas washing bottle containing a solution of ferric ammonium sulfate and 1,10-phenanthroline. Sulfur dioxide reduces the ferric ion to the ferrous form, which reacts with 1,10-phenanthroline to form an orange-colored complex. The absorbance of the colored solution is read in a spectrophotometer at a wavelength of 510 mμ, and the concentration present is read from a calibration curve.

Sampling Procedure

A sampling rate of up to 3 cfm can be used to collect the sample. The sample is collected until the color developed is sufficient for reading in the spectrophotometer. A concentration of 0.05 ppm can be determined in a 100-liter air sample.

Interferences

Hydrogen sulfide interferes with the determination of sulfur dioxide.

This method is applicable to ambient air analysis, and to industrial hygiene, stack gas and auto exhaust analysis for sulfur dioxide.

Selected Methods for the Measurement of Air Pollutants, U.S. Public Health Serv. Publ. No. 999-AP-11 (1965) p A-1.

See Also

West, P. W., and G. C. Gaeke. Anal. Chem. **28,** 1916 (1956).

Sulfur dioxide, in concentrations from approximately 0.005–5 ppm, can be determined by this method. The air sample is collected in a midget impinger containing sodium tetrachloromercurate solution. After collection, the sample is quantitatively transferred to a beaker and acid-bleached pararosaniline and formaldehyde are added. After

20 minutes the resulting red-colored solution is read in a spectro-photometer at a wavelength of 560 mμ. The quantity of sulfur dioxide present in the sample is read from a calibration curve prepared from sodium metabisulfite solution. The airborne concentration of sulfur dioxide is calculated.

Sampling Procedure

The sample can be collected in a midget impinger containing 10 ml of a sodium tetrachloromercurate solution. A sampling rate of 0.2–2.5 lpm is satisfactory. The sampling duration may vary from a few minutes to 24 hours.

Interferences

Heavy metals interfere by oxidizing the dichlorosulfitomercurate but this can be eliminated by adding ethylenediaminetetraacetic acid to the sampling solution. Sulfur trioxide and sulfuric acid also interfere.

Analysis requires approximately 2 hours to complete. This method is suitable for both industrial hygiene and air pollution work.

Hanson, N. W., D. A. Reilly, and H. E. Stagg, Eds.   *The Determination of Toxic Substances in Air* (Cambridge, England: W. Heffer and Sons Ltd., 1965), p 185.

Sulfur dioxide, in concentrations from 1–10 ppm in a 0.75-liter air sample, can be determined by this method. The air sample is collected in a midget impinger containing a solution of sodium hydroxide of known normality. After collection, hydrochloric acid and a Fuchsin–formaldehyde reagent are added and the optical density of the blue to violet color is read in a spectrophotometer at a wavelength of 540 mμ. The quantity of sulfur dioxide present is determined from a calibration curve prepared from solutions of sodium sulfite. The airborne concentration of sulfur dioxide is then calculated.

Sampling Procedure

The sampling rate through the midget impinger should be approximately 1 lpm until at least 1 liter of air has been sampled. A sensitivity of less than 1 ppm can be obtained by increasing the sampling time.

The method is simple, requiring approximately 1 hour to complete. No special or expensive equipment is required and the method is suitable for industrial hygiene work. The method may be used for the analysis of sulfur dioxide present as an air pollutant but the sampling time must be extended to at least 30 minutes.

Kniseley, S. J., and L. J. Throop. **p-Aminoazobenzene for the Spectrophotometric Determination of Sulfur Dioxide,** Anal. Chem. **38,** 1270 (1966).

This method was not designed specifically for air sampling but appears to be applicable. Sulfur dioxide in two concentration ranges, 0–10 and 10–100 μg, can be determined by this method. The editor suggests that the sample might be collected in a fritted bubbler containing 10 ml sodium tetrachloromercurate solution. The sample is quantitatively transferred to a 100-ml volumetric flask. Formaldehyde solution, *p*-aminoazobenzene solution and concentrated hydrochloric acid are added to the sample which is diluted to 100 ml with distilled water. After 10 minutes the absorbance of the sample is read in a spectrophotometer at a wavelength of 505 mμ. The quantity of sulfur dioxide present is read from a calibration curve, and the airborne concentration is calculated. Standards are prepared from sodium bisulfite.

Interferences

No mention is made of interfering substances although it is likely that ozone and nitrogen oxides will interfere to some extent.

The method requires approximately 1 hour for complete analysis. This method is applicable to both industrial hygiene and air pollution work.

Scaringelli, F. P., B. E. Saltzman, and S. A. Frey. **Spectrophotometric Determination of Atmospheric Sulfur Dioxide,** Anal. Chem. **39,** 1709 (1967).

The West and Gaeke method for the determination of sulfur dioxide is reviewed and modified to increase the reliability of the method as well as to extend the useful analytical range of the method. The method allows the determination of sulfur dioxide in the range of 0–35 ppm. Interferences from ozone, oxides of nitrogen, and heavy metals are minimized. The method is improved because pH, temperature, impurities in reagents, and water are strictly controlled.

Jacobs, M. B. *The Analytical Toxicology of Industrial Inorganic poisons* (New York: Interscience Publishers, Inc., 1967), p 528.

See Also

1. Fieldner, A. C., C. G. Oberfell, M. C. Teague, and J. N. Lawrence. Ind. Eng. Chem. **4,** 523 (1919).

2. Gardner, E. D., S. P. Howell, and G. W. Jones.   U.S. Bur. Mines Bull. **287** (1927).

Sulfur dioxide, in concentrations exceeding 0.5 ppm in a 50-liter air sample, can be determined by this method. The sample is collected in three impingers connected in series. The first bubbler contains a standardized iodine in potassium iodide solution, the second contains a standardized solution of sodium thiosulfate to capture any iodine escaping from the first bubbler, and the third contains water to collect any thiosulfate carried over from the second bubbler. After collection, the sample is quantitatively transferred to a beaker and an aliquot of the sample is titrated with standardized sodium thiosulfate solution. The airborne concentration of sulfur dioxide is calculated.

Sampling Procedure

The sampling rate should be 1–2 lpm through the three impingers. The duration of sampling will depend upon the concentration expected but at least 50 liters of air should be sampled.

Interferences

Hydrogen sulfide, acids, alkalies, and any material reacting with iodine will interfere with this determination.

The method is relatively simple and requires approximately 2 hours to complete. This time is required primarily to prepare the standardized solutions. The method is suitable for industrial hygiene work and is sufficiently sensitive for air pollution work provided that a relatively long sampling time is used.

Jacobs, M. B. *The Analytical Toxicology of Industrial Inorganic Poisons* (New York: Interscience Publishers, Inc., 1967), p 530.
See Also
1. Thomas, M. D., and J. N. Abersold.   Ind. Eng. Chem., Anal. Ed. **1**, 14 (1929).
2. Thomas, M. D.   Ind. Eng. Chem., Anal. Ed. **4**, 253 (1932).

Sulfur dioxide, in concentrations above approximately 0.1 ppm in a 1-cubic-foot air sample, can be determined by this method. The air sample is collected in two large fritted bubblers containing hydrogen peroxide in distilled water. After collection, the sample is quantitatively transferred to an Erlenmeyer flask and titrated with a standard sodium hydroxide solution using Bromophenol Blue as the indicator. The airborne concentration of sulfur dioxide is calculated.

Sampling Procedure

A sampling rate of 1–2 lpm through the fritted bubblers containing 100 ml of a hydrogen peroxide solution should be adequate for sample collection.

Interferences

Sulfur trioxide interferes with the determination but hydrogen sulfide does not. Any acid material will also interfere with this method.

The method is relatively simple and requires approximately 1.5 hours for complete analysis. The major portion of this time is used to prepare the required standardized solutions. The method is suitable for industrial hygiene analysis and can be used for air pollution analysis provided that a sufficiently long sampling period is used.

Jacobs, M. B. *The Analytical Toxicology of Industrial Inorganic Poisons* (New York: Interscience Publishers, Inc., 1967), p 531.

See Also

1. Thomas, M. D., and J. N. Abersold. Ind. Eng. Chem., Anal. Ed. **1**, 14 (1929).
2. Thomas, M. D., and L. Greenburg. Ind. Eng. Chem. **48**, 1517 (1956).

Sulfur dioxide, in concentrations exceeding 0.1 ppm in a 30-cubic-foot air sample, can be determined by this method. The sample is collected in a Greenburg-Smith impinger or a gas washing bottle containing 75 ml of a hydrogen peroxide solution which has been adjusted to a pH of 4.0. A few drops of an indicator mixture of Bromocresol Green and Methyl Red are added and the solution titrated to a green fluorescence. The air sample is then collected and the sample is quantitatively transferred to a flask and titrated with a standardized sodium hydroxide solution until the fluorescence reappears. The concentration of sulfur dioxide is then calculated.

Sampling Procedure

A sampling rate of 1 cfm for at least 30 minutes should collect a sample large enough for adequate analysis.

Interferences

Sulfur trioxide will probably interfere with this method. Any other acidic material will also interfere with this determination.

The method is simple and requires approximately 1.5 hours to complete. Most of this time is required to prepare the standardized solutions.

Jacobs, M. B. *The Analytical Toxicology of Industrial Inorganic Poisons* (New York: Interscience Publishers, Inc., 1967), p 534.

Sulfur dioxide, in concentrations above 0.1 ppm, can be determined with this method if a 30-cfm air sample is collected. The air sample is collected in a Greenburg-Smith impinger containing a standardized sodium hydroxide solution. After collection, the sample is quantitatively transferred to a flask and acidified with hydrochloric acid. The sample is then titrated with 0.001N iodine using starch as the indicator. The airborne concentration of sulfur dioxide is then calculated.

Sampling Procedure

A sampling rate of 1 cfm for at least 30 minutes is adequate for collection if a Greenburg-Smith impinger containing 75 ml of a standardized sodium hydroxide solution is used.

Interferences

Any reducing substance will interfere with this determination.

The method is relatively simple and requires approximately 2 hours for complete analysis. The major portion of this time is spent in standardizing the iodine solution. This also requires the standardization of a sodium thiosulfate solution against potassium dichromate. The method is suitable for industrial hygiene work and is sufficiently sensitive for air pollution work.

Jacobs, M. B. *The Analytical Toxicology of Industrial Inorganic Poisons* (New York: Interscience Publishers, Inc., 1967), p 535.

Sulfur dioxide, in concentrations above 0.1 ppm, can be determined if a 30-cfm air sample is collected. The air sample is collected in a Greenburg-Smith impinger containing a standardized sodium hydroxide solution. After collection, the sample is diluted to a known volume and quantitatively transferred to an Erlenmeyer flask. An aliquot of the sample is titrated with iodine to determine the approximate sulfur dioxide concentration. From this information an aliquot containing 30–60 μg of sulfur dioxide is diluted to 25 ml and placed in a Nessler tube. Fuchsin reagent is added and the sample diluted to 50 ml. The color development is allowed to proceed for 30 minutes, after which the optical density of the sample is read in a Klett-Summerson colorimeter equipped with a green filter. The quantity of sulfur dioxide in the aliquot is determined from a calibration curve previously prepared from sodium metabisulfite. The airborne concentration of sulfur dioxide is then calculated.

Sampling Procedure

A sampling rate of 1 cfm through the Greenburg-Smith impinger containing 75 ml of a standardized sodium hydroxide solution for 30 minutes should provide an adequate sample.

Interferences

The method is relatively specific for sulfur dioxide.

This method is relatively simple and requires approximately 3 hours to complete the analysis. It is suitable for industrial hygiene work and is sufficiently sensitive for air pollution work if a large air sample is collected.

Jacobs, Morris B. *The Analytical Toxicology of Industrial Inorganic Poisons* (New York: Interscience Publishers, Inc., 1967), p 562.
See Also
Jacobs, M. B., in *Air Pollution* (Ed. by L. C. McCale, New York: McGraw-Hill, 1952).

The air sample is collected in an impinger containing a solution of lead acetate in acetic acid. Any sulfite present is converted to lead sulfite and the sulfur trioxide to lead sulfate. The lead sulfite, being highly insoluble, forms a turbid solution which can be measured in a spectrophotometer at 600 mμ. The sample can be acidified and the sulfite concentration can be determined by an iodine titration. Total sulfate can be analyzed using a barium sulfate technique, and the quantity of sulfur trioxide present in the sample can be calculated by difference.

Cares, J. W. **The Determination of Oxides of Sulfur by X-ray Emission Spectrometry,** Am. Ind. Assoc. J. **29,** 386 (1968).

Sulfur oxides in the parts per million range can be determined by this method. The sample may be collected in midget or Greenburg-Smith impingers at the usual airflow rates. A suitable aliquot is treated to produce a barium sulfate precipitate. The sample and appropriate standards are analyzed by X-ray emission spectrometry.

Interferences

The method analyzes all sulfur oxides present and not any particular one. Suspended particulates may produce high results.

This method is suitable for air analysis as well as for analysis of stack gases.

Sulfur Monochloride

Jacobs, M. B.   *The Analytical Toxicology of Industrial Inorganic Poisons* (New York: Interscience Publishers, Inc., 1967), p 568.

Sulfur monochloride can be collected in silver nitrate acidified with nitric acid. The sample can be collected in a fritted bubbler at a rate of 2–3 lpm for 30 minutes. Following collection, sodium chloride is added and the sample is titrated with $0.1N$ silver nitrate. The airborne concentratio of sulfur monochloride is calculated.

The method requires approximately 2 hours for analysis. It detects approximately 1 ppm parts of air and is applicable to industrial hygiene work.

Sulfur Trioxide

Seidman, E. B.   **Determination of Sulfur Oxides in Stack Gases**, Anal. Chem. **30**, 1680 (1958).

Sulfur trioxide in concentrations exceeding 0.001% of total gas can be determined by this method. The sample is drawn through three absorbers, connected in series, each containing 80% isopropyl alcohol for absorption of the sulfur trioxide. The samples are immersed in ice water during sampling. An aliquot is used for analysis. Thorin indicator is added to the aliquot and the sample is titrated with barium chloride to a pink end point.

The sampling rate is 1 cubic foot of sample collected in 20 minutes.

Interferences

Interferences if present are considered to be negligible.

This method is applicable to the determination of sulfur trioxide in stack gas. A method for the determination of total sulfur oxides is also described.

Sulfuryl Chloride

Jacobs, Morris B. *The Analytical Toxicology of Industrial Inorganic Poisons* (New York: Interscience Publishers, Inc., 1967), p 570.

Sulfuryl chloride can be determined by almost any method used for the analysis of sulfate or chloride. These methods are described elsewhere in this book.

Tetrachloroethane

Hanson, N. W., D. A. Reilly, and H. E. Stagg, Eds. *The Determination of Toxic Substances in Air* (Cambridge, England: W. Heffer and Sons, Ltd., 1965), p 102.

Tetrachloroethane, in concentrations from 50–500 μg in 10 ml of sampling solution, can be determined by this method. The air sample is collected in a midget impinger containing 10 ml pyridine. After sampling, an accurately measured volume of a standardized sodium hydroxide solution is added to the sample which is then heated for 5 minutes in a water bath. After cooling, the optical density of the solution at 525 mμ is read in a spectrophotometer. The quantity of tetrachloroethane is read from a previously prepared calibration curve, and the airborne concentration of tetrachloroethane is calculated.

A sampling rate of 0.5 lpm should be adequate and a 0.5-liter sample should provide a sensitivity range of 50–500 μg in 10 ml of sampling solution. Concentrations higher or lower than the specified range may be obtained by increasing or decreasing the sample size.

Interferences

Chloroform and trichloroethylene may interfere with this determination.

The method is simple and rapid, requiring approximately 30 minutes to complete the analysis. It requires no special or expensive equipment and is suitable for industrial hygiene work. This method is not considered to be sensitive enough for air pollution work.

Tetraethyl Lead

Moss, R., and E. V. Browett. **Determination of Tetra-Alkyl Lead Vapour and Inorganic Lead Dust in Air,** Analyst **91,** 428 (1966).

Methods are detailed for the determination of tetraethyl lead, tetramethyl lead and particulate lead. Sampling periods of up to 8 hours will provide an accurate determination in the range of 1 μg lead per cubic meter of air. The particulate lead is collected on a filter while the tetra-alkyl compounds are collected in a bubbler containing iodine monochloride. The iodine solution breaks down the tetra-alkyl compounds to lead ions which are determined by a dithizone method. Any extraneous lead ions will interfere with this method.

The method is suitable for both industrial hygiene and air pollution work but requires a relatively long time for a complete analysis.

Snyder, L. J. **Determination of Trace Amount of Organic Lead in Air,** Anal. Chem. **31,** 591 (1967).

A method is provided to analyze tetraethyl lead in the parts per trillion range. A special sampling apparatus is used to collect the air sample. The organolead is converted to inorganic lead and determined by a dithizone method. A sample of 200 m^3 is collected at a rate of 0.7 cfm. The method requires several hours to complete but appears to be an excellent method for air pollution studies.

Toluene

Jacobs, Morris B. *The Analytical Chemistry of Industrial Poisons, Hazards and Solvents*, 2nd ed. (New York: Interscience Publishers, Inc., 1949), p 539.

See Also

1. Schrenk, H. H., S. J. Pearce, and W. P. Yant. U.S. Bur. Mines, Rept. Invest. 3287 (1935).
2. Pearce, S. J., H. H. Schrenk, and W. P. Yant. U.S. Bur. Mines, Rept. Invest. 3302 (1936).
3. Yant, W. P., S. J. Pearce, and H. H. Schrenk. U.S. Bur. Mines, Rept. Invest. 3323 (1936).

Toluene, in concentrations above approximately 25 ppm, can be determined by this method if a 0.5-liter air sample is collected. This limit can be extended by increasing the sampling time significantly. The air sample is collected by sampling through a special bubbler containing a nitrating acid composed of equal quantities of concentrated sulfuric acid and fuming nitric acid. After collection, the sample is allowed to react for 30 minutes to ensure complete nitration. The sample is quantitatively transferred to an Erlenmeyer flask and cooled below 20°C. It is neutralized by adding sodium hydroxide slowly and carefully. The solution is warmed to 30°C and 10 ml of methyl ethyl ketone (butanone) is added. The sample is transferred to a separatory funnel and the water drawn off. Sodium hydroxide is added and the color is allowed to develop for 1 hour. The resulting blue color changing to violet is compared with a set of standards and the quantity present in the sample is determined. The airborne concentration is calculated.

Sampling Procedure

The sample may be collected in a special bubbler containing nitrating acid. A sampling rate of 30 ml per minute for approximately 1 hour should provide a sufficient sample for analysis.

Interferences

Benzene, ethylbenzene, chlorobenzene, styrene and xylene will interfere with this determination.

The method requires approximately 3 hours for complete analysis. If a 60-minute sample is collected, the method is suitable for industrial hygiene work but is not sufficiently sensitive for air pollution work.

Moffett, P. A., T. F. Doherty, and J. L. Monkman. **Collection and Determination of Micro Amounts of Benzene or Toluene in Air,** Am. Ind. Hyg. Assoc. Quart. **17,** 186 (1956).

Toluene in quantities greater than about 0.5 mg can be determined by this method. The sample is collected by drawing the air through a tube containing silica gel. After collection the gel is immersed in isooctane and water added. The water displaces the aromatic hydrocarbon which dissolves in the isooctane. The absorbance is determined at 268.0 mμ in a spectrophotometer and the quantity present is determined directly from a calibration curve.

Sampling Procedure

The sample can be collected at a rate of 1 cfm for a period dictated by the concentration expected.

Interferences

Toluene must be the only hydrocarbon present because many other hydrocarbons will interfere.

The method is applicable to industrial hygiene work and requires less than 1 hour for completion of the analysis.

Dambrauskas, T., and W. A. Cook. **Methanol as the Absorbing Reagent in the Determination of Benzene, Toluene, Xylene and Their Mixtures in Air,** Am. Ind. Hyg. Assoc. J. **24,** 568 (1963).

Toluene, xylene, benzene and their mixtures can be determined in the parts per million range. The sample is collected in a gas washing bottle immersed in dry ice. The absorbing solution used is methanol. A rate of 1 lpm for 30 minutes will usually collect a suitable sample. After collection, the absorbance of benzene at a wavelength of 254.5 mμ, toluene at a wavelength of 268.5 mμ and xylene at a wavelength of 272.0 mμ was determined. A set of standards is prepared and the concentration of each component in the mixture is calculated.

Sampling Procedure

A gas washing bottle containing 50 ml of methanol is used to collect the sample. A sampling rate of 1 lpm for 30 minutes will usually provide a suitable sample.

Interferences

Any material absorbing at the wavelength of interest will interfere with the determination. The method is suitable for industrial hygiene work where concentrations are above 10 ppm. The method is not sufficiently sensitive for air pollution work. Analysis requires about 1 hour.

Hanson, N. W., D. A. Reilly, and H. E. Stagg, Eds. *The Determination of Toxic Substances in Air* (Cambridge, England: W. Heffer and Sons, Ltd., 1965), p 51.

Toluene, in concentrations from 40–350 ppm in a 0.25-liter sample, can be determined quickly and easily by this method. Increasing or decreasing the air sample volume will increase or decrease the concentration range to which the method is applicable. The sample is collected in a special U-tube containing a solution of formaldehyde and sulfuric acid. After collection, the sample is quantitatively transferred to a 25-ml volumetric flask and diluted to the mark with the formaldehyde–sulfuric acid reagent. The optical density of the color produced is read in a spectrophotometer at 445 mμ. The concentration in the sample is read from a calibration curve, and the airborne concentration of toluene is calculated.

The sampling rate through the U-tube containing the formaldehyde–sulfuric acid solution should be about 50 ml per minute for a period sufficient to collect about 250 ml.

Interferences

The method is not specific for toluene, and any aromatic hydrocarbon will interfere with this determination.

The method is simple and rapid, requiring about 1.5 hours to complete. No expensive equipment is required. The method is suitable for industrial hygiene work but is not sufficiently sensitive for air pollution work.

Tolylene Diisocyanate

Robinson, D. B. **Atmospheric Determination of Tolylene Diisocyanates**, Am. Ind. Hyg. Assoc. J. **23**, 228 (1962).

Tolylene diisocyanate (TDI) in concentrations above 0.05 ppm can be determined by this method. The sample is collected in a midget

impinger containing 0.6*N* acetic acid. Following collection, the sample
is diluted to 20 ml with 0.6*N* acetic acid, and dimethylaminobenzalde-
hyde in glacial acetic acid is added. The resulting bright yellow color is
allowed to develop for 1 hour. The transmission of the yellow-colored
reaction product is read in a spectrophotometer at a wavelength of 425
mμ. The concentration of TDI present is determined from a previously
prepared calibration curve.

Sampling Procedure

A sampling rate of 0.1 cfm through the midget impinger containing
15 ml of acetic acid reagent should be satisfactory. At least a 10-liter
air sample should be collected.

Interferences

Phenol above 40 ppm interferes with the reaction by depressing the
color formation.

The method is relatively specific for TDI and requires approximately
2 hours to complete. This method is applicable to industrial hygiene
and stack gas analysis. The method might be applied to air pollution
work provided that sufficiently large samples are collected.

Grim, K. E., and A. L. Linch. **Recent Isocyanate In-Air Analysis Studies,** Am. Ind. Hyg. Assoc. J. **25,** 285 (1964).

TDI, in concentrations from 0.01–0.08 ppm, can be quickly determined by this method. The air sample is collected in a midget impinger
containing 8 ml of a hydrochloric acid–acetic acid solution. A sodium
nitrite–bromide solution, sulfamic acid, and N-1-naphthylethylenedi-
amine is added to a 4-ml aliquot of the collected sample. The sample is
diluted to 5 ml with absorbing solution and the resulting blue-red solution is compared with a set of permanent color standards.

Sampling Procedure

The sample is collected at a rate of 0.1 cfm for 10 minutes. The pre-
cision, accuracy and sensitivity are within ±10% which is sufficient for
this application. If deemed necessary, the sensitivity and accuracy can
be improved by using a spectrophotometer to determine the color intensity.

The method is applicable to industrial hygiene work and in some
cases to air pollution work. The method requires approximately 30
minutes for completion. It is also possible to extend the range by
changing the size of the aliquot to be analyzed.

Hanson, N. W., D. A. Reilly, and H. E. Stagg, Eds. *The Determination of Toxic Substances in Air* (Cambridge, England: W. Heffer and Sons, Ltd., 1965), p 118.

TDI (tolylene diisocyanate), in concentrations from 0.01–0.04 ppm in a 5-liter air sample, can be determined by this method. A specially constructed absorber (described in the original reference) containing 3 ml of a solution of sodium acetate in hydrochloric acid is used to collect the air sample. At least 5 liters of air are sampled. After sampling, the absorbing solution is quantitatively transferred to a flask and a solution of stabilized *p*-nitrodiazobenzene is added. After shaking and allowing to stand for 5 minutes, 1.5 ml of chloroform is added and the resulting solution is shaken. The chloroform is taken off and placed in a test tube and the color produced is matched visually to a set of previously prepared standards. The concentration of TDI in the atmosphere is then calculated.

The sampling rate through the bubbler should be approximately 1 lpm and the duration should be about 5 minutes.

Interferences

MDI will interfere with this method of analysis.

The method is simple and rapid, requiring approximately 30 minutes for complete analysis. The method is considered suitable for industrial hygiene and air pollution analysis although a longer sample would probably be required for air pollution work. The sampling method used will provide a collection efficiency of about 76% and this must be considered when calculating concentration.

Hanson, N. W., D. A. Reilly, and H. E. Stagg, Eds. *The Determination of Toxic Substances in Air* (Cambridge, England: W. Heffer and Sons, Ltd., 1965), p 191.

See Also

1. Reilly, D. A. Analyst **88**, 732 (1963).
2. Marcali, K. Anal. Chem. **29**, 552 (1957).

Tolylene diisocyanate (TDI), in concentrations above 0.01 ppm, can be determined by this method. The sample is collected in a specially constructed low-volume gas scrubber containing 3 ml of *N,N*-dimethylformamide in dilute hydrochloric acid. After collection, the sample is quantitatively transferred to an Erlenmeyer flask, and sodium nitrite, sulfamic acid, and *N*-(1-naphthyl)ethylenediamine dihydrochloride solutions are added. The purple color produced is visually compared with a series of standards prepared from cobaltous chloride. The airborne concentration of TDI is calculated.

The sampling rate through the scrubber should be approximately 1 lpm for at least 3 minutes.

Interferences

The determination of TDI cannot be conducted in the presence of foams or lacquers because a cloudy solution results.

The method is simple and rapid, requiring approximately 10 minutes to complete. It is suitable for both industrial hygiene and air pollution work.

Levin, V. B., B. W. Nippoldt, and R. L. Rebertus. **Spectrophotometric Determination of Primary Aromatic Amines with Thiotrithiazyl Chloride,** Anal. Chem. **39,** 581 (1967).

Tolylene-2,4-diisocyanate, at concentrations exceeding 0.01 ppm, can be determined by this method. The sample is collected in a midget impinger containing $0.01N$ hydrochloric acid. The sample is quantitatively transferred to a flask and the pH adjusted to 10–11 with sodium carbonate. The sample is extracted with chloroform. Approximately 0.5 ml of this extract is placed in a spot plate and treated with solid thiotrithiazyl chloride and a few drops of methanol. The red color produced is compared with a series of paper strips and calibrated by comparison with colors produced from toluene-2,4-diamine. The concentration of TDI in the atmosphere is calculated.

Sampling Procedure

The air sample may be collected in a fritted bubbler containing 10 ml of $0.01N$ hydrochloric acid. A sampling rate of 2.8 lpm for 10 minutes should collect a sample adequate for analysis.

Interferences

Some of the primary aromatic amines will interfere with this method. The method requires less than 1 hour to complete and is applicable as a rapid field method for the determination of TDI. It is applicable to industrial hygiene work and also is sufficiently sensitive for air pollution work.

Reilly, D. A. **A Test Paper Method for the Determination of Tolylene Diisocyanate Vapour in Air,** Analyst **93,** 178 (1968).

Tolylene diisocyanate (TDI), in concentrations from 0.01–0.10 ppm in a 5-liter air sample, can be determined by this method. The air sample is drawn through Whatman filter papers impregnated with a solution consisting of 2-hydroxy-1,1,H-benzo(a)carbazole-3-carboxy-*p*-anisidide, sodium nitrite, ammonium acetate, and diethyl phthalate in methyl alcohol.

The air sample is drawn through the impregnated filter paper at the rate of approximately 1 lpm for 5 minutes. In the presence of TDI, a red-brown color appears which is compared with a series of colored standards prepared from red, blue and yellow pigments. The concentration of TDI in air is calculated.

Interferences

The following isocyanates interfere with the determination of TDI: (1) 4,4′-diisocyanatodiphenylmethane; (2) 1,5-diisocyanatonaphthalene; and (3) 4,4′-diisocyanate-3,3′-dimethylbiphenyl.

The method is simple and rapid, requiring approximately 15 minutes to complete if the standards are prepared first. The method is sufficiently sensitive for both industrial hygiene and air pollution analysis.

Meddle, D. W., D. W. Radford, and R. Wood. **A Field Method for the Determination of Organic Aromatic Isocyanates in Air,** Analyst **94,** 369 (1969).

Tolylene-2,4-diisocyanate (TDI), in concentrations from 0.0–0.4 ppm, can be determined by this method. The sample is collected in a small fritted bubbler containing dimethylformamide in dilute hydrochloric acid. After collection, a solution of sodium nitrite and bromide, sulfamic acid and N-1-naphthylethylenediamine is added to the sample. The resulting color is compared with color standards or the absorbance is read in a spectrophotometer. The concentration of isocyanate is then calculated.

Sampling Procedure

The air sample is collected in a small bubbler at a rate of 1 lpm for 10 minutes. This procedure should provide a sufficient sample for analysis.

Interferences

Other isocyanates and any primary amine will interfere with this determination.

The method requires approximately 45 minutes to complete. The procedure is applicable to both industrial hygiene and air pollution work.

m-Toluidine

Hanson, H. W., D. A. Reilly, and H. E. Stagg, Eds. *The Determination of Toxic Substances in Air* (Cambridge, England: W. Heffer and Sons, Ltd., 1965), p 56.

m-Toluidine in concentrations above 1 μg per 10 ml of hydrochloric acid sampling solution, can be determined quickly and easily by this method. The sample is collected in a fritted bubbler containing 10 ml of a standardized hydrochloric acid solution. The sample is quantitatively transferred to a volumetric flask. A sodium nitrite solution is added and allowed to stand for 15 minutes at a temperature below 15°C. Sodium sulfamate, sodium acetate, N-sulfatoethyl-*m*-toluidine and hydrochloric acid are added. Full color development occurs in 10 minutes. The optical density of the solution is read on a spectrophotometer at a wavelength of 505 mμ. The quantity of *m*-toluidine present is determined from a previously prepared calibration curve, and the airborne concentration is calculated.

The sampling rate through the fritted bubbler should be approximately 5 lpm. Sampling time depends on the expected concentration of the amine.

Interferences

Many amines and their derivatives interfere with this method.

The method is relatively simple and requires about 2 hours for complete analysis. No special or expensive equipment is required. The method is suitable for industrial hygiene work.

Tributylphosphine

Bolton, N. E., J. B. Johnson, W. H. McCermott, and U. T. Stack, Jr. **Determination of Tributylphosphine in Air**, Am. Ind. Hyg. J. **20**, 32 (1959).

Tributylphosphine, in concentrations exceeding 1 ppm, can be determined by this method. The air sample is collected in a cold trap. After collection, the sample is allowed to warm to room temperature and a mixture of potassium dichromate and sulfuric acid in distilled water is added. The sample is raised to a temperature of 180°C for 15 minutes, cooled and maintained at 100°C for 15 minutes, and cooled again to room temperature. Methanol is added to destroy the excess dichromate and the sample is diluted to 100 ml with distilled water. An aliquot of the sample containing less than 40 μg of phosphorus is quantitatively transferred to a beaker. The pH is adjusted to 1.25 with ammonium hydroxide. The sample is transferred to a separatory funnel and diluted to 40 ml with sulfuric acid. Ammonium molybdate and butyl alcohol are added and mixed thoroughly. The lower layer is discarded and the upper layer is washed with sulfuric acid, which is also discarded. Stannous chloride is added and the lower layer again discarded. A 10-ml aliquot of the butyl alcohol layer is diluted to 20 ml with methyl alcohol, and the absorbance of the resulting blue color is read on a spectrophotometer at 730 mμ. The quantity of phosphorus present is read from a calibration curve, and the airborne concentration of tributylphosphine in the atmosphere is calculated.

Sampling Procedure

The sample is collected in a cold trap immersed in a dry ice–acetone mixture. An air sample of 2–5 liters should be collected. One trap can be used to collect a sample at the rate of 50 ml per minute, two traps at a rate of 100 ml per minute, or three traps at a rate of 500 ml per minute.

Interferences

No discussion of interferences is provided. It is evident, however, that any phosphorus-containing material will interfere with this determination.

Analysis requires approximately 2.5 hours to complete. The method is applicable to industrial hygiene analysis.

Trichloroethylene

Jacobs, Morris B. *The Analytical Chemistry of Industrial Poisons, Hazards and Solvents*, 2nd ed. (New York: Interscience Publishers, Inc., 1949), p 562.

See Also
Patty, F. A., H. H. Schrenk, and W. P. Yant. Ind. Eng. Chem.,
Anal. Ed. **4,** 259 (1949).

Trichloroethylene, in concentrations exceeding 50 ppm parts of air, can be determined by this method. The air sample is collected by mercury displacement and then introduced into a special combustion apparatus. The chloride produced by this procedure is collected. The sample is titrated with a standardized silver nitrate solution and the resulting precipitated silver chloride is removed by filtration. The solution is back-titrated with a standardized potassium thiocyanate solution using ferric alum as the indicator. The airborne concentration of methyl chloride is then calculated.

Interferences

The method is not specific for trichloroethylene, and many halides can be determined by this method.

The determination requires about 3 hours to complete. This method is suitable for industrial hygiene work even though the lower limit of it is 50 ppm. This method of analysis is not sufficiently sensitive to be used in air pollution analysis.

Jacobs, Morris B. *The Analytical Chemistry of Industrial Poisons, Hazards and Solvents,* 2nd ed. (New York: Interscience Publishers, Inc., 1949), p 590.
See Also
1. Barrett, H. M.   J. Biol. Chem. **18,** 341 (1936).
2. Ross, J. H.   J. Biol. Chem. **58,** 641 (1923/24).
3. Cole, W. H.   J. Biol. Chem. **71,** 173 (1926).

Trichloroethylene, in concentrations exceeding 20 ppm, can be determined by this method. The sample is collected in a fritted bubbler containing absolute ethyl alcohol. After collection, 10 ml of the sample is quantitatively transferred to a 50-ml volumetric flask and diluted to that mark with distilled water. Five ml of the diluted sample is placed in a test tube along with a pyridine–sodium hydroxide solution. The sample is heated in a water bath for 5 minutes and the resulting orange color is compared with a series of color standards. The concentration is calculated from the closest standard.

Sampling Procedure

The sample can be collected in a small fritted bubbler containing absolute ethyl alcohol. A sampling rate of 0.5 lpm for 30 minutes should be adequate.

Interferences

Any method with a similar molecular configuration will interfere with this method. Examples are bromoform, iodoform, Chloretone, chloral, and pentachloroethane.

The method requires about 1 hour to complete and is accurate only to approximately ±20% of the amount present. This method is not sufficiently sensitive for use in air pollution analysis.

Stack, V. T., Jr., D. E. Forrest, and K. K. Wahl. **Determination of Trichloroethylene in Air,** Am. Ind. Hyg. Assoc. J. **22,** 184 (1961).

Trichloroethylene, in concentrations above approximately 1 ppm, can be determined by this method. A grab sample is collected using an evacuated 250-ml gas sampling tube. After collection, the sample is cooled and toluene is added. After being warmed to room temperature, the sample is drained into a graduated cylinder. A 1-ml aliquot is quantitatively transferred to a stoppered flask and pyridine and alcoholic potassium hydroxide are added. After 15 minutes, methanol is added and the optical density of the resulting solution is read in a spectrophotometer at a wavelength of 537 mμ. A set of standards are similarly treated and a calibration curve is constructed.

The method is suitable for industrial hygiene work and requires approximately 1 hour to complete the analysis.

Hanson, N. W., D. A. Reilly, and H. E. Stagg, Eds. *The Determination of Toxic Substances in Air* (Cambridge, England: W. Heffer and Sons, Ltd., 1965), p 101.

Trichloroethylene, in concentrations from 50–500 μg in 10 ml of sampling solution, can be determined by this method. The air sample is collected in an impinger containing 10 ml of pyridine. After sampling, an accurately measured volume of a standardized sodium hydroxide solution is added to the sample, which is then heated for 5 minutes in a water bath. After cooling, the optical density of the solution at 440 mμ is read in a spectrophotometer. The quantity of trichloroethylene is read from a previously prepared calibration curve and the airborne concentration of trichloroethylene is calculated.

A sampling rate of 0.5 lpm should be adequate and a 0.5-liter sample should provide a sensitivity range of 50–500 μg in a 10-ml aliquot of sampling solution. Concentrations higher or lower than the specified range may be obtained by increasing or decreasing the size of the air sample.

Interferences

Tetrachloroethane and chloroform may interfere with this determination.

The method is simple and rapid, requiring approximately 30 minutes for completion. This method requires no special or expensive equipment and is suitable for industrial hygiene work. It is not considered sufficiently sensitive for air pollution work.

Trichloronitromethane

Jones, L. R., and J. A. Reddick.   **Colorimetric Determination of Nitroparaffins,** Anal. Chem. **24,** 1533 (1952).

Trichloronitromethane, in concentrations above 3 μg in the sample analyzed, can be determined by this method. The sample may be collected in two fritted bubblers containing concentrated sulfuric acid. An aliquot of the sample, up to 10 ml, is quantitatively transferred to a test tube and held in a boiling water bath for 5 minutes. After cooling, resorcinol solution is placed on top of the acid and the sample slowly mixed. The sample is heated in a water bath and cooled. The optical density of the resulting red-blue color is read in a spectrophotometer at a wavelength of 560 mμ. The quantity of trichloronitromethane present is read from a calibration curve, and the airborne concentration is calculated.

Sampling Procedure

The sample may be collected in two bubblers, series-connected, containing sulfuric acid. A sampling rate of 2 lpm for a period long enough to collect 5–10 μg will provide an adequate sample.

Interferences

Any aliphatic nitroparaffin will interfere with this determination. Analysis requires approximately 30 minutes to complete. This method is suitable for industrial hygiene work, and, if a sufficiently large sample is collected, it is also applicable to air pollution work.

Triethylamine

Dahlgren, G. **Spectrophotometric Determination of Ethyl-Diethyl and Triethylamine in Aqueous Solution,** Anal. Chem. **36,** 596 (1964).

Triethylamine, in the parts per billion range, can be determined by this method. The samples should be collectable in distilled water in a standard impinger. A 25-ml aliquot is used for analysis. Sodium bicarbonate, hypochlorite solution, nitrite solution and standard potassium iodide are added to the sample. The absorbance of the color is read at 540 mμ in a spectrophotometer.

Sampling Procedure

The sampling rate can probably be as high as 1 cfm through the standard impinger containing 75–100 ml distilled water.

Interferences

Aniline and possibly some of the other amines interfere with the procedure. The method should require about 1 hour or less.

Triethylene Glycol

Wise, H., T. T. Puck, and H. M. Stral. **A Rapid Colorimetric Method for the Determination of Glycols in Air,** J. Biol. Chem. **150,** 61 (1943).

Triethylene glycol, in the parts per million range, can be determined by this method. The sample is collected in two series-connected Folin tubes immersed in a test tube containing distilled water. After collection, an aliquot of the sample is quantitatively transferred to a large test tube which is immersed in cold water. Ten ml of a potassium dichromate in sulfuric acid solution is added and the sample heated in a boiling water bath for 15 minutes. The intensity of the resulting green color is read in a colorimeter at a wavelength of 616 mμ. The quantity of triethylene glycol is determined from a calibration curve and the airborne concentration calculated.

Sampling Procedure

A flow rate of 20–30 lpm is satisfactory. The duration of collection must be timed to collect at least a 300-liter sample.

Interferences

Any reducing material will interfere with this determination.

The method requires less than 2 hours to complete the analysis and is suitable for industrial hygiene work. This method probably is not suitable for air pollution work because of the long sampling time that would be required and because of interferences that would be present.

Trifluoroacetic Acid

Franklin, M., R. Scherberger, H. Brockmyre, and D. W. Fasset. **Determination of Acetic Acid in Air**, Am. Ind. Hyg. Assoc. J. Quart. **17,** 221 (1956).

Trifluoroacetic acid, at concentrations below 1 ppm, can be determined by this method. The sample is collected in an impinger containing an absorbing solution of glycerol, water, Methyl Purple indicator and an antifoam agent. The absorbing solution is calibrated by titrating with acetic acid until the indicator color changes from the original green to purple. Air is sampled until this same color change takes place, and the concentration of trifluoroacetic acid is calculated.

Sampling Procedure

A sampling rate of 0.1 cfm provides satisfactory collection when a midget impinger is used. At acid concentrations above 15 ppm, the time required for the color change must be accurately noted because a few seconds error in recording the time of the appearance of the end point will cause an appreciable error. In order to overcome this difficulty it is possible to use larger volumes of absorbing solution or lower airflow rates.

Interferences

Most acids will react in the same manner; therefore, only one acid must be present in the atmosphere to be analyzed. Carbon dioxide does not interfere at concentrations below 5000 ppm.

The method is applicable to industrial hygiene analysis and requires less than 1 hour to complete.

4,6,8-Trimethylazulene

Sawicki, E., T. W. Stanley, and W. C. Elbert. **Spot Test Detection and Spectrophotometric Determination of Azulene Derivatives with 4-Dimethylaminobenzaldehyde,** Anal. Chem. **33,** 1183 (1961).

4,6,8-Trimethylazulene can be determined in concentrations as low as one part 4,6,8-trimethylazulene in five million parts of sample solution. No data were presented on collection methods but it appears that a sample could be collected in ethyl or methyl alcohol. A solution of 4-dimethylaminobenzaldehyde in acetic acid is added to the alcoholic sample. Hydrochloric acid and trichloroacetic acid are added and the resulting blue color is allowed to develop for 15 minutes. The absorbance is read in a spectrophotometer at 620 mμ and compared with a standard curve.

No information on sampling rates is given but 1 cfm through a Greenburg-Smith impinger containing 75–100 ml alcohol appears to be reasonable.

Interferences

Other azulene compounds will interfere. Pyrroles and indoles are the other main possible interferences.

The method is sufficiently sensitive to be used for air analysis. Analysis requires about 30 minutes.

2,4,6-Trinitrotoluene

Pinto, S. S., and J. P. Fahy. **A New Colorimetric Method for the Determination of TNT (2,4,6-Trinitrotoluene) in Air,** J. Ind. Hyg. Toxicol. **24,** 24 (1942).

2,4,6-Trinitrotoluene can be determined in concentrations exceeding 0.1 mg per m^3 of air in the dust state or its equivalent in the vapor state.

The air sample is collected in a midget impinger containing 10 ml isopropyl alcohol. A 5-ml aliquot is used for analysis. Concentrated sulfuric acid and titanous chloride are added to the aliquot, and the sample is heated in a boiling water bath. This procedure reduces the TNT to triaminotoluene. The color is produced by adding sodium nitrite, ammonium sulfamate and dimethyl-α-naphthylamine to the reduced sample. The transmittance of the resulting pink-to-red color is read in a spectrophotometer. The quantity of TNT present in the 5-ml aliquot is determined from a calibration curve.

Sampling Procedure

The sampling rate through the impinger is 0.1 cfm for 20 minutes. If concentrations less than 0.1 mg per m³ need to be determined, the sampling duration can be extended.

Interferences

Theoretically compounds such as tetryl and dinitrophenol can interfere with this method.

The method can be used in industrial hygiene work and in other areas where TNT might be expected to be found in concentrations exceeding about 0.1 mg per m³. The method is quantitative and requires about 3 hours for completion.

Goldman, F. H., and D. E. Rushing. **Diethylaminoethanol as a Reagent for the Detection and Colorimetric Determination of Small Amounts of Trinitrotoluene in Air,** J. Ind. Hyg. Toxicol. **25,** 164 (1943).

2,4,6-Trinitrotoluene, in concentrations above 5 μg per ml of sampling solution, can be conveniently determined by this method. The sample is collected in a midget impinger containing 10 ml diethylaminoethanol until a distinct red-violet color is observed. The absorbance is determined at a wavelength of 400 mμ and the results compared to a previously prepared calibration curve.

Sampling Procedure

The sampling rate through the midget impinger should be maintained at or below 0.1 cfm. Sampling should be continued until a definite color is observed.

Interferences

Dinitrotoluene will not interfere with this method. No other possible interferences are discussed.

The method is quantitative and relatively simple. The time required for analysis is about 1 hour. This method is suitable for industrial hygiene work and other areas where elevated concentrations may be found.

Turpentine

Jacobs, Morris B. *The Analytical Chemistry of Industrial Poisons, Hazards and Solvents,* 2nd ed. (New York: Interscience Publishers, Inc., 1949), p 533.

Turpentine, in the parts per million range, can be detected by this method. The air sample is collected in a bubbler containing 95% ethyl alcohol. After collection, the sample is transferred to a volumetric flask and diluted to the mark with alcohol. A 5-ml aliquot is transferred to a suitable container and a solution of vanillin in hydrochloric acid is added. After 30 minutes the blue-to-green color developed is compared with a series of standards. The airborne concentration is calculated.

Sampling Procedure

The sample is collected in a bubbler containing 95% ethyl alcohol at a rate of 0.5 lpm. The sample duration should be at least 1 hour.

Interferences

The method is not specific because some of the constituents of turpentine will give the same reaction. Benzene, benzine, acetone and butanone, carbon monoxide and acrolein do not interfere.

The method requires approximately 1 hour to complete. It is suitable for industrial hygiene work but is not sufficiently sensitive for air pollution work.

n-Valeraldehyde

Albrecht, A. M., W. I. Scher, Jr., and H. J. Vogel. **Determination of Aliphatic Aldehydes by Spectrophotometry,** Anal. Chem. **34,** 398 (1962).

n-Valeraldehyde can be determined quantitatively at concentrations below 0.4 moles per ml of sampling solution.

The air sample may be collected in a midget impinger containing 10 ml of distilled water. To an aliquot of this sample is added a solution of methylamine hydrochloride in sodium pyrophosphate followed by the addition of a solution of *o*-aminobenzaldehyde. The absorbance of the yellow-colored reaction mixture is read at 440 mμ in a spectrophotometer. The quantity present is read from a calibration curve.

The sampling rate may be 0.1 cfm through a midget impinger or 1 cfm through a standard impinger. Scrubbers or gas washing bottles may be used. A sampling duration of 30 minutes will usually collect a suitable sample.

Interferences

Other aliphatic aldehydes interfered and many of them can be determined by this method.

The method is useful for atmospheric sampling and analysis and should be adaptable for use at stack concentrations. Analysis requires approximately 1 hour.

Xylene

Jacobs, Morris B. *The Analytical Chemistry of Industrial Poisons, Hazards and Solvents*, 2nd ed. (New York: Interscience Publishers, Inc., 1949), p 544.

See Also
1. Schrenk, H. H., S. J. Pearce, and W. P. Yant.   U.S. Bur. Mines, Rept. Invest. 3287 (1935).
2. Pearce, S. J., H. H. Schrenk, and W. P. Yant.   U.S. Bur. Mines, Rept. Invest. 3302 (1936).

Xylene, in concentrations above approximately 25 ppm, can be determined by this method if a 0.5-liter air sample is collected. This limit can be extended by increasing the sampling time significantly. The air sample is collected by sampling through a special bubbler containing a nitrating acid composed of equal quantities of concentrated sulfuric acid and fuming nitric acid. After collection, the sample is allowed to react for 30 minutes to ensure complete nitration. The sample is quantitatively transferred to an Erlenmeyer flask and cooled below 20°C. It is then neutralized by adding sodium hydroxide slowly and carefully. The solution is warmed to 30°C and 10 ml of methyl ethyl ketone (butanone) are added. The sample is transferred to a separatory funnel and the water drawn off. Sodium hydroxide is added and the color is allowed to develop for 1 hour. The resulting blue color is compared with a set of standards and the quantity present in the sample is determined. The airborne concentration is calculated.

Sampling Procedure

The sample may be collected in a special bubbler containing nitrating acid. A sampling rate of 30 ml per minute for approximately 1 hour should provide a sufficient sample for analysis.

Interferences

Benzene, ethylbenzene, chlorobenzene, styrene and toluene will interfere with this determination.

Analysis requires approximately 3 hours to complete. If a 60-minute sample is collected, the method is suitable for industrial hygiene work, but it is not sufficiently sensitive for air pollution work.

Dambrauskas, T., and W. A. Cook. **Methanol as the Absorbing Reagent in the Determination of Benzene, Toluene, Xylene and Their Mixtures in Air,** Am. Ind. Hyg. Assoc. J. **24,** 568 (1963).

Xylene, toluene, benzene and their mixtures can be determined in the parts per million range. The sample is collected in a gas washing bottle immersed in dry ice. The absorbing solution used is methanol. A rate of 1 lpm for 30 minutes usually will collect a suitable sample. After collection, the absorbance of benzene at a wavelength of 254.5 mμ, toluene at a wavelength of 268.5 mμ and xylene at a wavelength of 272.0 mμ are determined. A set of standards is prepared, and the concentration of each component in the mixture is calculated.

Sampling Procedure

A gas washing bottle containing 50 ml of methanol is used to collect the sample. A sampling rate of 1 lpm for 30 minutes will usually provide a suitable sample.

Interferences

Any material absorbing at the wavelength of interest will interfere with the determination. The method is suitable for industrial hygiene work where concentrations are above 10 ppm. It is not sufficiently sensitive for air pollution work and requires about 1 hour to complete the analysis.

Hanson, N. W., D. A. Reilly, and H. E. Stagg, Eds. *The Determination of Toxic Substances in Air* (Cambridge, England: W. Heffer and Sons, Ltd., 1965), p 51.

Xylene, in concentrations from 40–350 ppm in a 0.25-liter sample, can be determined quickly and easily by this method. Increasing or decreasing the air sample volume will increase or decrease the concentration range to which the method is applicable. The sample is collected in a special U-tube containing a solution of formaldehyde and sulfuric acid. After collection, the sample quantitatively is transferred to a 25-ml volumetric flask and diluted to the mark with the formaldehyde–sulfuric acid reagent. The optical density of the color produced is read in a spectrophotometer at 460 mμ. The concentration in the sample is read from a calibration curve, and the airborne concentration of xylene is calculated.

The sampling rate through the U-tube containing the formaldehyde–sulfuric acid solution should be about 50 ml per minute for a period sufficient to collect about 250 ml.

Interferences

The method is not specific for xylene and any aromatic hydrocarbon will interfere with this determination.

The method is simple and rapid, requiring about 1.5 hours to complete the analysis. No expensive equipment is required, and the method is suitable for industrial hygiene work but not sufficiently sensitive for air pollution work.

2,4-Xylidine

Jacobs, Morris B. *The Analytical Chemistry of Industrial Poisons, Hazards and Solvents,* 2nd ed. (New York: Interscience Publishers, Inc., 1949), p 714.

Xylidine, in concentrations above approximately 2 ppm in a 2-liter air sample, can be determined by this method. The sample may be collected in a fritted bubbler containing dilute sulfuric acid. After collection, the sample is evaporated almost to dryness, treated with hydrogen peroxide and allowed to cool. The sample is diluted with distilled water. Nessler's reagent is added and after 5 minutes the resulting color is read in a spectrophotometer at a wavelength of 425 mμ. The quantity of xylidine present is read from a calibration curve and the airborne concentration calculated.

Sampling Procedure

The sample may be collected in a midget impinger containing 20 ml of water acidified with two drops of sulfuric acid. A sampling rate of 0.2 lpm for 10 minutes usually will collect a sufficient sample.

Interferences

Any material releasing ammonia will interfere with this method.

The method requires approximately 2 hours for complete analysis and is suitable for industrial hygiene work. This method probably is not sufficiently sensitive for air pollution work.

Hanson, H. W., D. A. Reilly, and H. E. Stagg, Eds. *The Determination of Toxic Substances in Air* (Cambridge, England: W. Heffer and Sons, Ltd., 1965), p 56.

2,4-Xylidine in concentrations above 1 μg per 10 ml of hydrochloric acid sampling solution, can be determined quickly and easily by this method. The sample is collected in a fritted bubbler containing 10 ml of standardized hydrochloric acid solution. The sample is quantitatively transferred to a volumetric flask. A sodium nitrite solution is added and allowed to stand for 15 minutes at a temperature below 15°C. Sodium sulfamate, sodium acetate, N-sulfatoethyl-*m*-toluidine and hydrochloric acid are added. Full color development occurs in 3 hours. The optical density of the solution is read on a spectrophotometer at a wavelength of 505 mμ. The quantity of 2,4-xylidine present is determined from a previously prepared calibration curve and the airborne concentration is calculated.

The sampling rate through the fritted bubbler should be approximately 5 lpm. The duration of sampling depends on the expected concentration of the amine.

Interferences

Many amines and their derivatives interfere with this method.

The method is relatively simple and requires about 2 hours to complete the analysis. No special or expensive equipment is required, and the method is suitable for industrial hygiene work.

The text of this book was typeset at SSPA Typesetting, Inc., Carmel, Indiana, in 10-point Caledonia. The chapter headings are in 14-point Craw Modern. The printing and binding was done by offset lithography by LithoCrafters, Inc., Ann Arbor, Michigan.